THE
CHAINED
DOMINANT

One Man's Journey to Find His Confidence

ALEXANDER D. BANKS

PROLOGUE

She was in ecstasy, spinning and floating, as her head slumped back as far as the D-ring would allow. Lost in our roles, we'd both forgotten we were on a stage and that others watched. I switched to my favorite cane and surprised her with a quick wrist flick that stunned her. She gasped and cried out, but her body shuddered in deep appreciation as she tried to catch her breath again. I knew just how much pressure to apply, just what she liked, just enough pressure for her desires to run wild. As I raised thin red welts on her bare ass and thighs, I sought to bring blood to the fleshy, meaty areas, but not to draw blood, only to pleasurably warm those spots.

A few unexpected cane flicks always did the trick. I kept my submissive from entirely slipping into a foggy subspace where I might not reach her. I closely watched her reactions and controlled my pressure and caning intensity to keep my submissive on a heady rollercoaster as she straddled pain and pleasure, unable even to hold up her head anymore. I skillfully maintained control over her ride as she pleaded and moaned for more. When her eyes had fully glazed over, I knew she'd gone over the ledge into that deep erotic abyss.

She was mine, entirely, wholly, mine. But she felt ready for more, she wanted more, so much more. I had only warmed her up.

I grabbed a short length of chain and connected it to a suspended ceiling hook. Then I attached the D-ring at the neck of her straitjacket, but not enough to jerk her neck or hurt her. My goal was only to restrict her movement to just below the ceiling hook and to keep her guessing about what would come next. I put a red ball gag in her mouth, only so the dungeon monitor wouldn't be summoned. As my submissive looked away from me, I picked up my favorite leather whip and brought it down hard! It tore into the bare flesh of her firm, pink ass cheeks. Her screams were not heard over the music and through the ball gag, as her mind scrambled and panicked to decipher pain from pleasure. But before clear answers could be assimilated, the next lashing kissed her red thighs. Tears ran down her cheeks as her head fell forward.

"Do you know who your sir is?" I whispered in her ear as I held her soaking-wet hair back from the side of her face. She couldn't answer, couldn't even focus on me or my voice. She blinked her eyes ever so slowly. Her blank stare told me she knew. I'd given her what she'd wanted, what she'd needed, and somewhere amid the tangle of pain and pleasure, we had both found what we'd been seeking. As I unchained her, she fell limp into my arms. I removed the restrictive straitjacket from her trembling, sweaty form. She couldn't stand. She was unable to speak. I wrapped the sheet around her naked, damp body, and then I helped her to a nearby sofa. She lay still and silent, unable even to lift her hand. I picked it up and held it as I cradled her limp form against me. She was mine, entirely mine, *all mine.*

CHAPTER 1

GROWING UP IN THE SHADOWS

It's true what they say about how stuff rolls downhill. The last of the litter of eight kids, I was used to being picked on by my siblings, always at the bottom. Oddly, although we were a huge family, I was the only child Mom and Dad had together. You'd think that might have counted for something, but maybe that bothered my sisters and brothers so it counted against me.

Born and raised in Bonney Lake, a city about forty miles from Seattle, Washington, as the crow flies, I didn't think my childhood was that unusual at the time. But as I got older and looked back, from a different vantage point, I have to say, we were a screwed-up bunch. We were perfectly imperfect, each with our own quirks, oddities, and idiosyncrasies that made us unique—or downright peculiar, as the case may have been for a few members of our clan.

Take Dad, for instance; he did some unusual things. Like the day he cleared out all the old photos of my brothers' and sister's mom from their house—and then he moved in a new woman with her daughter, Krissy, and said, "Here you go, kids! Here's your new mom, and she comes with a new blonde little sister for you, too!" Dad's first wife had been a drinker who had gotten into a car accident and died from her injuries. But when she was gone, Dad was ready to move on, too, without a second thought to how his kids might feel about him simply replacing their mom with a new model.

When Dad removed all the old photos, the kids were stupefied as they looked back and forth at each other. Their immediate attitude toward the new woman was, "You're not my mother!" Well, as it turned out, she *was my mother* because she got pregnant with me and I soon joined the family. That led to the older kids' initial resentment of me, the kid who belonged to the strange woman Dad had brought into their house.

While our dad may have been tactless and thoughtless at times, there was no denying Dad had always been good in business, and that trait seemed to run in the family. As a kid, I heard stories of how my grandfather had owned a construction business in 1918, the largest one west of the Mississippi, and since he'd made money in construction, he also saw excellent promise in the timber industry. He had three sons, but two of them didn't get along. It was said the sons had different personalities, goals, and values, and since everyone is not meant to be an entrepreneur, the brothers couldn't work together. The family had lumber yards in Portland and Seattle, and by 1943, they decided to split up the lumber yards and go their separate ways. This story would be of interest to me later because I'd be embroiled in a similar story with my own brothers.

As a boy, I got very little attention. With eight kids and only so many hours in a day, I guess my parents didn't have much time left for young Alexander. Yet they always found time for one another. No, they made time for one another. They were each other's main priority. Mom and Dad regularly went to dinner or out dancing. They frequently took trips to Hawaii, and they indulged in life's finer things.

My brother Bobby didn't care for my mom when she and Dad married. Bobby fought with her all the time. At the time, Dad was a World War II navigator, and he could be tough on his kids. He frequently berated them in front of their friends and embarrassed them. When the kids went to Mom about how Dad treated them, she always said, "You've just got to accept your dad for the way he is." But the kids didn't agree, not at all. Before long, Dad's poor treatment of his kids caused people not to want to be around Mom and Dad, and even kids didn't want to come around our house for fear Dad would go off on someone with one of his merciless rants.

Bobby couldn't wait to turn seventeen. When he did, he petitioned the court to become an emancipated minor. He left home and went to live with his girlfriend's parents as soon as the court granted his petition. Bobby had found his freedom, but he and our parents would not talk again for nearly twenty-five years.

My brother Steve fell in line more easily and didn't rock the boat. He got married and went into the family timber business. But our brother John wouldn't even get that option.

When John was just thirteen, he was diagnosed with leukemia. Our parents tested all the kids to find the best option for a donor for a bone marrow transplant for John. But when the blood test results came back, they weren't what Dad had expected to hear.

"Sir, I don't know how to tell you this," the doctor said, "but we've run the tests several times, just to be sure, and it appears that two of the children are not blood-related to John, or therefore, to you, sir. It is biologically impossible that Tim and Cathy are your children. I'm sorry."

So, while one son had left home and refused to speak to him, and another young son lay dying of cancer, Dad had learned that two more of his children were not really *his children*. Half of Dad's world had imploded. Yet he told no one of the blood test results. As far as Dad was concerned, Tim and Cathy were his son and daughter and he would raise them as his own. But months after being broadsided with this life-altering news, we lost John before his fourteenth birthday. I would wonder later if Dad felt like he'd lost several children at that time as he struggled to hold his secret inside himself.

Krissy, my mom's biological daughter, was always Mom's jewel, her shining star. But thankfully, I had Irene, our live-in nanny, who was like a second mother to me. Maybe she noticed how Mom fawned and doted on Krissy, and how my face always fell when I watched Mom lavish attention on my sister. Irene often came and wrapped her arms around me and gave me extra-big hugs when she saw me watching how Mom adored Krissy. If Mom praised Krissy's artwork or told her how talented she was, Irene inevitably dropped what she was doing and came over to compliment my coloring or congratulate me on something she'd noticed. There were times when I wondered if Irene did it to make me feel better, or because she really meant the nice things she'd say, but then, as a kid, I didn't care so much. I was just grateful to have been noticed. Irene was my shining star, my savior, that special grownup who on some days made the difference in whether my bottom lip quivered. As a boy, I couldn't articulate to her what she meant to me, but I thought she knew. We had a special bond, that unseen love that went unsaid.

One day, Irene picked me up after school at 12 p.m., took me home, and made lunch for both Krissy and me. Krissy had stayed home due to not feeling well. I looked forward to seeing Irene at the end of the school day and showing her my papers. Krissy did, too, and Irene was always just as nice to Krissy as she was to me. She loved both of us the same. Around Irene, I never had to compete with Krissy. I always felt equal to my sister and as good as her. It was only around Mom that I felt I didn't measure up.

"Where's Krissy?" I asked the next day when Irene came for me after school.

"She's home sick," Irene said. "When we get home, you can go and wake her up and I'll make you both some lunch."

Irene went straight to the kitchen as I ran into Krissy's bedroom. Our collie looked up when I went into her room, but Krissy didn't stir from where she lay sleeping atop her twin bed.

"Krissy? Hey!"

I pulled off her slipper as I shook her foot, but my sister still didn't move. Our dog Tina looked at me expectantly, and then at Krissy. I couldn't understand why Krissy wouldn't wake up, so I hit the sole of her foot. But still, there was no response. I turned and went back to the kitchen.

"She won't wake up," I said.

"I'll go and get her in a minute. You just wash your hands at the sink."

Irene continued preparing sandwiches for lunch, probably thinking Krissy was simply sleeping. After she finished making my sandwich, she cut it in half and placed the plate in front me where I sat at the kitchen table. I took a bite and watched as Irene finished making Krissy's lunch. After she'd put away the mayonnaise and wiped off the countertop, she turned to go wake Krissy. I jumped up to follow her and show her how deeply my sister had been sleeping when I'd tried to revive her.

But this time, when we got to Krissy's room, my sister was foaming at the mouth and nose. Irene instantly ran for the phone and dialed for help. It seemed like everything changed within nanoseconds—my home, my family, and my life. Irene shifted into high-gear and my home became a whirlwind of medics, flashing lights, and mayhem. All around me, pandemonium swirled as I quietly watched in fear. Even as the medics worked on Krissy, I knew. Irene's pale, distressed face said it all, as she waited for Dad to pick up the phone in Hawaii. I knew how utterly devastated my mom would be when she heard the news. Krissy was her favorite and Mom had never tried to hide that fact.

While tears streamed down her face and her hand shook, Irene spoke into the phone to Dad as I watched and listened. The shift in the house was noticeable, almost like an earthquake. Even the air smelled different as Irene's words relayed what the medics said as they worked on Krissy.

"They can't revive her either. She's totally unresponsive," Irene repeated as she sobbed. "They're trying, yes!"

Krissy was taken by ambulance to the hospital and the medics worked feverishly on her, even as they wheeled her outside. No one was willing to give up on a little girl. Irene hung up the phone and told me my parents would be on the next flight home from their Hawaiian vacation. I knew when Krissy left our home that she would never be back; a piece of me went with her that day. The tall, uniformed sheriff took me aside and tried to explain to me what was happening. His mouth moved, but I really didn't hear his words. It was all surreal. I couldn't digest any of it. I just wanted Krissy to wake up, put on her slippers, and then get up and play with me, just like she'd always done. Then the immortal words rang aloud in my ears. "Son," he said, "your sister has died. She's gone." With those short words, my world collapsed and I fell to the floor in a daze, tears streaming from my face, so distraught that no words could escape my mouth under the flood of crushing tears.

Mom and Dad were, of course, so incredibly devastated by the loss of Krissy that they didn't see or recognize how her death hit me. Since my other siblings had always treated me like crap, and Krissy had been my only friend in the house, I was all alone after she'd gone. The doctors told my parents that a blood vessel in the back of Krissy's head had burst while she'd been asleep, a *cerebral hemorrhage*, they'd called it. All I knew was that my best friend, the only sibling I had felt remotely close to, was forever gone and I was on my own.

As Mom's biological daughter, Krissy had been her princess and her pride and joy. My mom didn't know how to live without Krissy in the world. It was like life had stopped for Mom, too, when Krissy had stopped breathing. Krissy had been Mom's whole life and the reason for her existence. We'd all known it, but after Krissy had died, Mom seemed to wither, and the lights went out in her eyes.

With Krissy gone, Mom was forced to move to the kid in the #2 spot, the backup child, one might say. I felt like the consolation as Mom tried to fill the void left by Krissy's death with me. Yet no one seemed to notice that I, too, was lost, sad, and suffering without my sister. And it became overwhelmingly burdensome to be the "fallback kid" Mom used to try to ease the pain of her own loss. While Krissy had been alive, it was no secret she'd been Mom's favorite. So, with her gone, I felt like second best as Mom focused her attention and energy on me, while constantly comparing me to perfect Krissy, her golden child who was no longer here. The longer Krissy was gone, the more perfect her memory became in Mom's mind. I would never measure up since the bar continued to be moved and because my Mom glorified the memory of her beautiful blonde daughter.

As time went on, Krissy's memory became more exalted and Mom placed her on a pedestal in her mind. Yet as much as my mom missed Krissy, the empty place in Mom's heart couldn't compare to my own bottomless abyss of pain. My parents sent me to a psychologist after I lost my sister. But in time, I'd learn that professionals can only give patients tools and instruction. People have to dig deep, experience life, overcome all the crap in their immediate lives, and do the hard work once they've left the psychologist's office. The answer for me did not lie within the four walls of my psychologist's office. In fact, it would be years before I'd unearth certain keys and truths about myself.

Maybe it was the time I'd been born into that affected how I would move in the world and how I would integrate into life. My parents weren't unlike millions of other Americans who embraced a traditional, old-school lifestyle. Following the radical 1960s and then the countercultural shake-ups of the 1970s, like the Vietnam War and the Watergate scandal, many people wanted to live a sedate, suburban existence. But for countless people, the white picket fence and the welcome wreath on their freshly-painted front doors were facades, merely props that hid what lay just beyond all the prettiness. Mom and Dad wanted us to be good citizens, God-fearing Christians, and moral individuals—and if we couldn't *be* those things, then for the love of God, we'd better make sure we *appeared* to be that way!

For the most part, America was still a place of conservatism, at least in our area of the country, and our parents expected we would shape up and fall in step, no questions asked. America may have eased her grip on her idealistic dreams of the 1960s and 1970s, but in Dad's house, things would be done his way. And if it was a Martini Night when he came home from work, we all knew what to expect. Dad was a man who never minded sharing his opinions, and his mouth had no governor. More times than I can even count, Dad embarrassed me with his verbal abuse, admonishments, and name-calling. He never cared if we had friends over, if we were out-side and within earshot of the neighbors, or if his bitter diatribe completely humiliated us in front of anyone. This was always of interest to me since Dad seemed to want his home and family to appear well-maintained, pristine mirrors of how well he'd done in life. Maybe when Dad verbally attacked us, it was his way of assert-ing dominance and cementing his position at the top of his family's food chain. But to a little kid, a father's repeated verbal assaults, reminders of his faults and failures, and hurtful name-calling work like water eroding a rock face. A child can't unhear those things. He can't make himself stop feeling the gut-twisting pain of his own father's words that felt like blows, and he plays them over and over, each time reliving the pain.

"Why does Dad do that?" we'd cry to Mom.

"Oh, that's just how he is. We just have to let him be and not worry about it. We've just got to accept your dad for how he is."

Even as a kid, Mom's explanation seemed utterly insane to me. But crazier still was that ten minutes after Dad had totally shredded and eviscerated me, he'd walk back into the room as if nothing had happened. Yet the ugliness of his words hung on me like a heavy, hot tar I could never remove. It was a painful burden I'd carry for years. Even as I'd try to tuck it away, it would poke out and, at times, become difficult to lug around.

Always a chunky boy, I used food as a source of comfort. I relished my afternoons watching *Gilligan's Island* with a couple of gooey Snickers bars. Life was good as I lost myself in the mouth-watering peanut, caramel, and milk chocolate and immersed myself in the castaways' antics on the TV screen. But I didn't play Little League baseball or other organized sports, so the candy bars and sedentary activities weren't the best idea for a stocky kid.

Tensions often ran high in our house. My older siblings resented me, the silver spoon in the mouth child who linked their dad to my mom, the kid who had come along two years after their father had married the woman who'd replaced their real mother after she'd died in a drunken car accident. I always felt pressure. It was on me, around me, and inside of me. After Krissy died and Mom focused all her attentions on me, her lone surviving biological child, that pressure increased. My stepsiblings didn't like me, my dad was always tough on me, and my mom always needed me. Even breathing became difficult at times. It was hard to tell if my weight was smothering me, or if it was all the emotional baggage I carried.

"You're not my *mother! You can't tell me what to do!*"

That was a regular shriek, heard several times weekly in our home. But if I were lucky, I could turn up the TV's volume and drown out my siblings' screams as they argued with Mom. My mother had a tough role. She wasn't their biological mother, it was true, but they were lucky she'd come along and tried to step into their mom's role. Hers was a thankless role—she was damned if she did and damned if she didn't. She'd never win, and even Mom knew it.

CHAPTER 2

SCANDALOUS

After going to a private Lutheran school through the eighth grade, I knew I needed to branch out and explore what it really meant to be a teenager. I knew that meant going to a public school and forcing myself outside of my comfort zone. It would be somewhat scary, at first, but it would be worth it, too. My parents agreed to enroll me in a public school with hundreds of teens in its student body. And speaking of student body, my own was a rather large-framed, big-boned one. I was a big guy when I started high school, six-foot-two and 265 pounds, but I was fortunate to carry it well.

"Banks!" the football coach always called to me, in the most hopeful voice as he hopefully eyed my massive stature. "You sure you don't want to join our team, man?"

"No, thanks, Coach!" I always laughed.

Nope. Football was not for me. But I definitely looked the part of a wide-shouldered, brawny linebacker, very capable of holding my own and holding the line. I'm sure when the coach saw me, he envisioned me hoisting a refrigerator over one shoulder with ease, while eating a bologna sandwich with my other hand. It must've killed him that he'd been unable to recruit "that giant of a kid" onto his team. But I hadn't grown up playing organized sports, and then after losing Krissy, life had been especially difficult for me.

My remaining siblings were all older and busy with their own lives, and Mom and Dad had each other. That left me, Alexander D. Banks, the pudgy, emotional boy who'd always felt like something had been missing. Such a statement sounds like sheer insanity, even to me, given that I grew up wanting for virtually nothing. We had everything and anything kids could want or need: the nice house, new cars, clothes, electronics, waterfront property, help in our home, and so much more. Our parents were those country clubber socialites who enjoyed their martinis and mixers with all the other well-to-do suburban couples. Stylishly dressed and immaculately coiffed, they hobnobbed with their friends at the club who raised their glasses and toasted a record-setting day in the market, the grand opening of a new office location, or a recent corporate promotion. The women all wore the latest fashions, sparkling jewels, and the newest hairstyles, straight from the pages of *Vogue* and the other women's magazines they devoured. The men presented in tailored suits, expensive blazers, sharp trousers, Italian leather shoes, and gold watches. Depending on the occasion, they'd wear Parisian silk ties or tuxes, but always within tasteful guidelines. The holidays were usually when everyone shined, that time of year when women went to their safe deposit boxes to retrieve their best jewels to wear for the parties and galas. It was easy to tell which husbands had received the biggest annual bonuses by which wives had the most impressive bling. The women enjoyed being the envy of the other ladies, just as much as the men basked in the glory that they'd had a record year and all their golf buddies and associates knew it. Of course, many years would pass before I would connect all the dots and figure out all the hidden agendas, oblique innuendos, and phony facades of such things. At the time, it was simply our life and what we knew.

Life was odd, though, especially after I lost Krissy. Even the way I was told of her passing had been weird, like something that could have been handled differently. I guess there's no right way to tell a little kid that his sister is gone forever. But I played that scene over, and over, in my head. I'd never forget how that sheriff had told me my beloved Krissy was dead, forever gone from my world. That moment of standing in the utility room, just he and I, while all the hustle and bustle was going on behind the uniformed man, had left a marked, indelible defining line in my life, a dividing point that I'd always see as "before Krissy died" and "after Krissy died." More times than I can count, I'd wish to be able to jump across that damned line and return to the other side, to the "before Krissy died" side of my life.

It was probably like that for Mom, too. Her heart was clearly broken when she lost her precious blonde daughter. Without Krissy to hold onto, Mom held even tighter to me, her only remaining biological child. But she did me no favor since my brothers and sister already didn't like me very much. Mom's over-the-top, exaggerated favoritism toward me gave them yet another reason to resent me. She probably thought she was showering me with her love. To me, though, Mom's constant attention was smothering and burdensome, like a heavy, wet blanket I never could remove, no matter how hard I fought and struggled. Life became hellish for me. On top of the pain of missing Krissy, my siblings' resentment of me, and Dad's gruff demeanor, my mom's ceaseless suffocation made life mentally torturous and lonely.

Maybe Cathy, my sister, felt lonely in her own way, too, or maybe she simply liked sex. Whatever the reason for her constant basement hookups, Cathy wouldn't have time to think about it for long because she soon became pregnant at sixteen. Such a transgression in our home was right up there with capital murder. But there was no body to bury. There was a baby on the way, and Mom and Dad could not risk the scandal that would surely ensue if the country clubbers got wind that sixteen-year-old Cathy was anything but a vestal virgin.

"What will people say?" My mom swooned with all the theatrics of an actress who'd just reclined on her fainting couch.

"They will say nothing!" Dad said. "She's leaving town and right away!"

I listened with great curiosity to see just how they planned to keep people from knowing Cathy was with child. But it seemed our parents had a plan.

"Cathy, you will go to Seattle," Dad told her.

"What?" Cathy responded in shock.

"It's okay," Mom said. "There's a midwife and you will receive care. You'll go through your pregnancy there, and once the baby's born, you will place it for adoption, and you'll return home."

"Right. We'll just say…" Dad began, but he couldn't decide how to finish.

"We can say she's gone to study abroad," Mom offered. "Kids do it all the time."

Cathy had no choice and no say in the matter. Mom and Dad made all the arrangements. She would be shipped off to Seattle to some home for unwed girls where a midwife would care for her until she gave birth, and then Cathy would give up her baby for adoption. She'd then return home, appearing to still be an unspoiled, chaste teen girl, as if nothing had happened.

But Cathy had always marched to her own beat. She was sort of a flower child, that girl with an independent streak who saw the world through unique eyes. I doubt that at sixteen she was in love with her baby's father, but carrying a child and then giving birth would have a great impact on Cathy. No amount of fashionable clothes, cultured activities, or hoity-toity club parties would be able to fix her, not ever. Cathy would have her baby, alone in Seattle, and then return home to our family, her uterus and her heart forever changed. A few years later, she'd leave for college, seeking to fill that painful void and, not surprisingly, become pregnant once again. But this time, Cathy married her baby's father and they had a second child later, too. Her husband was an odd one, though. Maybe she'd gravitated to a dysfunctional guy because she'd come from our dysfunctional home. I'm no psychologist, but believe me, with my experience, I know dysfunction when I'm *in* it. In the end, Cathy's marriage failed and even her relationship with her kids wouldn't be very good. It was like she'd perpetuated the screwed-up family life of her own childhood. We'll never know, but I have to wonder if it could all be traced back to having been forced to give up her first baby. The rest of us were, of course, sworn to silence and secrecy. No one, absolutely no one, could ever know of Cathy's moral misstep lest it become a blemish on the family reputation. It merely became more of the burden we were told to carry and never share.

When we went to church, we looked like a spit-polished, perfectly normal American family, cloaked in our pristine church clothes. But our garb hid our dysfunction and our secrets, and as we grew older, our clothes felt tighter and more uncomfortable. At least, that's how it felt to me. To be fair, though, there were good times in our family. Some of my best memories were of days spent with Dad, just the two of us, fishing on the lake behind our home.

My dad really wanted to help me fulfill my dreams. One time, when I told him I wanted to raise guppies, Dad jumped in and helped me do it. Even doing chores with my dad made some good memories. Dad was often the tree trimmer and I was the clean-up kid, the one who picked up the branches and trimmings. Yet as we worked, Dad and I talked, and I got to spend time with my father. Since he and Mom were often together, dining, dancing, or on trips, I appreciated when Dad made time for me.

My parents took me to Hawaii at least twenty times, but most times, they liked to go together, just the two of them. During those times, Irene looked after me. She was an important part of my childhood, that special lady whose presence made a huge difference in my world. We loved it when my parents arranged big family picnics or threw huge parties, like on the Fourth of July. Our home on the lake was the perfect backdrop for get-togethers and barbecues. Yet as my siblings got older and moved out, those times became fewer and farther between. I missed them and a new kind on loneliness set in. Our house seemed bigger than ever and far too quiet. Now it wasn't just Krissy who was missing from my world, it was everyone who had gone on with their lives and left me.

In time, I realized I had a choice. I could be more personable, more like I'd watched my father be, especially in his business relationships. I knew if I emulated what I'd watched my dad do, I could force myself to become more sociable and outgoing. I'd put myself in more situations with opportunities to be around people. Since I had always hated to waste time, I vowed to jump in all at once and make my efforts count when I enrolled in my new public high school.

Socially awkward, I was that teenager who tried to fit in and find my place. I worked at it like it was my job, with a dedication

I'd take into my adult life. It was something important to me. I'd do whatever necessary to break through the barriers and get beyond the outer fringes of the social circles. Although I worked hard at infiltrating the popular social cliques at school, I found that no matter how hard I worked to fit in, I couldn't quite get to where I wanted to be. I was just different. Quiet, overweight, and naturally withdrawn, I didn't even like myself, so how could I get others to like me? How could I get girls to find me interesting?

I'd seen a psychologist since my sister's death and the counseling had been of some help. But no amount of counseling would ever fill the void Krissy's death had left inside of me or within our family. Mom would never be the same and neither would I. Hell, the world would never be the same after that dreadful day when we lost my sister. Frankly, I was surprised it still even rotated. Not much had seemed to make sense after we'd lost Krissy, although everyone had robotically gone on with their life's functions.

In years to come, I'd realize people had perceived our family as one of the fortunate ones; we were the well-to-do kids who had been born with silver spoons in their mouths. But what others don't realize is that kids like us have to work twice as hard and shine twice as bright to prove ourselves. Anything less looks as if our successes have been given to us and not earned by our own hands and sweat. I began to realize this as a young adult, maybe even when I was still in high school. It was important for me to earn my success and prove myself worthy of it, even to myself.

But first, I had to check something off my list, like most teen boys. I'd had my first wet dream thanks to Kristy McNichol, the popular teen actress at the time, but I was still a virgin. At seventeen, I decided to remedy that situation, and I took the easy way out by asking the quiet, frumpy girl at school for a date. There was no way she'd decline, and there was no chance she'd have other plans for the weekend. In fact, the unattractive, fat girl leapt at the chance to go out with me. I would look back years later and regret this for so many reasons. But at the time, I was a teenage boy with just one focus. Stacey was also a virgin, and the time we spent together was more important to her than to me. That was one of the reasons I'd look back with heavy regrets on what had, at the time, been the best five minutes of my life. I'm sure Stacey recalls all the details of our intimacy in the vacant house where she and I lost our virginity together. But I simply checked off the box as I moved into man-hood—or so I thought, at the time. Years later, I would learn the importance of respect and love when being intimate with a woman, and the epiphany would make me realize I'd cheated both Stacey and me out of sharing that experience with our first loves. I expect Stacey realized the same, or I hope she did because it would mean she eventually found real love, which she deserves. She surely deserved better than some high school guy who'd just needed her for five minutes to lose his virginity. I'm sure I broke Stacey's heart, and I'm really not proud of how I treated her. I suspect a lot of Staceys are out there, just like there are plenty of selfish teen boys with tunnel vision.

When high school ended and it was time to head off for college, I was on my own. Mom and Dad had a laissez-faire attitude of letting life take its own course. They were ready to wave goodbye and let me fly wherever the winds might take me. But I'd grown up as a sheltered kid. I felt like I was being thrown out into the world or dropped from 30,000 feet into the ocean and told to sink or swim. My friends' parents had been doing college tours, making future plans, and providing guidance and direction. But my mom and dad left it up to me. Their attitude was, "You've got the whole state! Pick a college!"

Without a clue of what was beyond our immediate lifestyle and my family's life experiences, I packed up my Toyota Forerunner with all the belongings I might need for college. My buddies' moms had been buying them dorm necessities, clothes, school supplies, furnishings, and all the comforts of home. But Mom thought I had it all under control and I'd buy whatever I needed. I was a guy. How did I know what I needed until I needed it? It terrified me that I didn't know what I needed! In fact, it terrified me that I didn't know *what I didn't know*! But Mom and Dad were blissfully at ease as they waved me off. I watched them get smaller in my rearview mirror as they waved and smiled, "Have a great time at college, Alex! See ya!"

It felt like I was driving into the great unknown, possibly to my doom. I had no clue what to expect at the university. I'd come from a comfortable home in which I'd been well-provided for my entire life, although dysfunction had run rampant. Each one of my family members was screwed-up in their own unique way. Some of us shared some of the same issues and commonalities, but I'd always been the different one among the siblings. So why should college be any different? Why should I expect to feel embraced or at home once I'd moved into my dorm when I'd never fit in with my own family? I had five hours to think about life as I drove toward the future and whatever might lay ahead. I willed the twisted knot in my gut to relax since I had no other choice.

When I pulled into the university on move-in day, so many parents were helping their sons and daughters move into their dorms. Mothers and fathers carried boxes, lamps, cheap furniture, bedding, and suitcases as I carried my own stuff through the dorm hallway and found my assigned room. I saw a few items I hadn't thought to bring and made a mental note to go to the local Walmart to pick them up. Who knew to bring a shower caddy, scatter rugs, or a closet organizer? Those must be items mothers had purchased prior to move-in day, I deduced. I saw fathers hanging pictures and posters on their kids' walls, so I made a mental note to pick some up for my room, but I'd have to hang them myself.

Since I had less items to unpack than most, I finished setting up my room fairly quickly. I walked around the dorm building and socialized a bit, introduced myself to some guys, and then walked out to check out the campus. I hated being so far from home. It felt weird and I was unnerved. There was a huge disconnect for me since my parents weren't with me to settle me in. Maybe they thought I could handle it, or maybe since they'd already had all the others leave home before me, they didn't think it necessary to take me by the hand. Whatever the case, it was an odd feeling to be alone on the campus of Western Washington University; it was the first time I had been away from the only family I'd known.

CHAPTER 3

FIRST LOVE

Being a college freshman on a gigantic campus was a new experience to all the freshmen. But I felt like a fish out of water, still the odd-man-out, that kid who just didn't fit in with the others. My social ineptitude made me feel awkward and uncomfortable, like I wanted to run for the hills and make a break for it. I tried hard to force myself to socialize and make friends, but I wasn't feeling better by the end of the first year when I turned my Forerunner toward home.

"You told us you were liking college," Mom said when I got home to our house. "I don't understand."

"It was okay. I just want to do community college for a while, I think," I explained. "I want to be closer to home for a while, that's all. I liked college, just not how far away it was, the distance."

After I took a short break during summer and took the next quarter off, I signed up for classes at the nearby community college. I felt more comfortable there, and after I took some classes, I decided to branch out again, this time to Bellingham, just two hours away from home. The distance seemed like a comfortable compromise. So, off to Bellingham I went to continue my education and my maturation. Once again, I forced myself to socialize and make friends. I even had some fun, which included the usual college hi-jinks like taping a guy to the inside of an elevator in the girls' dorm building one night. It was all in good fun, and it may, or may not, have involved a healthy infusion of alcohol to get the party started.

I was not one of the most seasoned guys on campus when it came to the dating department. But there was one thing I agreed with the other guys on—the girls at that college were extremely fond of themselves. They earned their moniker as "Belleview Bitches," let me tell you; and when they clustered together like hens, one could almost see the golden aura they exuded. They felt they glowed like goddesses and that the guys should fawn and fight over them. I wasn't half as impressed with them as they were with themselves. Maybe that was why one girl caught my eye one day. She stood out from the others. In her full-length gray coat, she was as cute and attractive, but not as full of herself, as the other girls.

"See that girl?" I said to my roommate as I nodded at her. "I'm gonna marry her."

"Yeah, whatever," he laughed.

After she'd walked off, I went and spoke to a friend about her. I asked if he knew the cute girl in the gray coat.

"Yeah, that's Naomi," he said.

"Well, I think I need to know Naomi."

Days passed, and I didn't see her again, but I kept my eyes peeled. One night, I went to a party, and to my surprise, Naomi opened the front door of the party house, where everyone was al-ready getting drunk inside. I introduced myself and went inside and grabbed a drink. People were playing quarters and tossing back beers. But I wasn't interested in the drinking games. I wanted to talk to the cute girl.

"Hey, do you want to go for a walk?"

"My mom warned me about being alone with strangers," Naomi said with a half-laugh, "and to be careful of guys. She said I could be raped."

"Well, we've met. I'm Alex. So, I'm not a stranger, right? And, I promise you will be okay with me."

She looked me up and down as if trying to make up her mind about her chances if she were to accept my promise about her personal safety. I guess I passed muster because she nodded that I should follow her, and we walked outside. Naomi and I walked and talked for a while and got to know each other. In no time, we realized our families belonged to the same country club, just a couple of hours away. Naomi seemed to feel more comfortable with me, and she even laughed a few times. I liked the way her eyes lit up when she laughed. I wanted so badly to kiss the cute girl, but I wasn't sure how to go about it, and I didn't want to screw it up. We continued to walk and talk some more.

Finally, thanks to the buzz I had, I worked up my nerve and went in for a kiss. Naomi easily returned it, and my confidence soared that the cute girl seemed to be into me. I felt like I was walking on air after that kiss. She and I walked back toward the party, but I walked slower on the way back, in no hurry for my time with Naomi to end.

When we got back, our buzzes had worn off, but Naomi turned to me and said, "I'd really like to see you again, Alex." Of course, I tried to play it cool when I agreed that I, too, would like to see her again. But I'm sure I rocketed home after her declaration. My feet barely even touched the ground after Naomi went inside! Cute Naomi wanted to see *me* again! *Jackpot!* I was smitten, bitten by the love bug—I had it bad for the girl. Without much experience with other girls, my emotions were colliding inside and washing over me, drowning me like a rogue tidal wave. But I enjoyed every minute of what was happening to me.

I took every opportunity to be with Naomi, even while she studied. Completely enamored with her, I loved being with the girl who quickly held my heart. She studied her books and I studied Naomi, content just to be with her. I fell fast and hard. But it was different for her. In fact, after the first time we'd met, when she saw me the next time, Naomi had recalled my name as something similar, but not my exact name.

"Allen!" she said. "Good to see you!"

"Uh, no. It's Alex," I corrected, a bit deflated.

But she and I still began to date, and I worked on her. Naomi and I seemed to solidify our relationship. As far as I was concerned, life had begun to fall into place. I'd met a girl, fallen in love, and was meant to be with her, the only one for me, even though I hadn't had much experience with other girls, much less too much life experience, in general. All I wanted to do was be with Naomi. All I thought about was Naomi. All that mattered to me was Naomi. I became that "Velcro-boyfriend," the clingy, impossible-to-shake, joined-at-the-hip guy whose girlfriend couldn't do anything without him at her side. I looked for any excuse to spend time with Naomi, dates or otherwise. We spent a lot of time just talking over pie and coffee since I've always preferred talking over watching TV or reading to pass the time.

Maybe Naomi realized I'd become too attached and much too fast. One afternoon, the words that came from her lips cut through me like a hot knife through butter. She said, "I just don't want a boyfriend right now." Naomi was a studious girl, intent on getting good grades, and working hard on her studies. But I couldn't focus on anything other than how her words had made me feel. The message delivered to my brain was, "Alex, you're not good enough to be my boyfriend. You're too fat. You're worthless. You're unattractive. You're fat. You're not of the same caliber as the guys whom Naomi dates. What were you thinking?" The message wasn't delivered in Naomi's voice. It was that same age-old, nagging voice that had plagued me for years, that unseen voice that had stalled my progress and held me back from breaking through the social barriers during high school. I'd always been on the outer fringes, on the outside and looking in at the popular, confident, attractive kids. Even now, although I was on a college campus, I still felt like that loser kid who couldn't measure up.

"Oh, yeah, sure," I said. "I get it."

I had to play it cool in front of Naomi, even though my heart had just been trampled and I felt as if I'd been eviscerated. It hurt so deeply to think I might never have cute Naomi in the long gray coat after all. In my mind, I'd already made life plans for us. We already had a house and children and we'd grow old together. I may not have had a great example of a traditional marriage during my own childhood, but I'd planned to construct one, and Naomi had been handpicked to be my wife. But I guess I hadn't considered that my wife would want a say in the matter.

· · ·

After that day, I fell into a depression. It was hard to let go of the ideal of a future with Naomi. I tried to go to my classes, and I forced myself to try to socialize with people. Yet all I thought about was Naomi and what could have been, what I'd lost. Fortunately, while my childhood may have been unconventional and dysfunctional in many ways, I had learned some valuable lessons from my dad, lessons he had likely learned from his own father. I'd watched Dad's tenacity for my whole life and his determination never to give up when he wanted something. There had to be a way. I had to find a way to be with Naomi.

Once I'd made up my mind that I had a plan, I felt better, at least somewhat. I had a goal, and that settled my mind and gave me a new focus. Everywhere I went, I kept my eyes peeled for Naomi. As eager as I was to see her, I knew I couldn't rush her or crowd her. She'd said she didn't want a boyfriend, so I didn't want to smother her or spook her. All I wanted was a chance, just an opportunity to be with the only girl I'd ever felt that way about. Eventually, I got my chance and Naomi agreed to a date, and then another one, and another one after that, and so on. I vowed to myself that I would not let her get away, not this time. Naomi had dated more than I had, but I didn't care. As far as I was concerned, I'd found the one and she was it. When you know, you know, as the saying goes.

My world revolved around the cute girl who still had all my attention. She continued to be what I thought of when I opened my eyes in the morning, and she was my last thought each night as I fell asleep. But I thought that was how it was supposed to be when a guy fell for a girl. I'd have done anything to keep that good feeling and to keep Naomi.

"What are you doing?" I asked her one day as I lay on Naomi's bed, watching her.

"Just studying."

"Want to come over her?"

I gave her a wry smile and waited for her reply.

"And do what?" she laughed.

"We can play strip poker," I suggested.

"I don't know how to play that one."

"Great, we can play backwards. We'll start with our clothes off, and as you win, you can put your clothes back *on*."

When Naomi told me she wanted me to meet her parents, I took it as a good sign. Since her parents were divorced, I would meet her mother in her mom's home. Like all guys do, I carefully dressed, shaved, and got ready to impress the mother of the girl I intended to marry. Naomi had told me all about her parents' breakup and her dad's infidelity, and how it had affected her own life. She'd also shared with me that she never wanted to get married, have kids, and then hurt them with divorce like her parents had done to her.

The moment Naomi's mom opened her front door, she caught me entirely off-guard as if I'd been hit by a bus and left with whiplash. "Oh, Naomi! You didn't tell me Alex has dimples!" she gushed. But in the same breath, she looked me square in the eye and said, "If you give my daughter AIDS, I'll kill you!" That was when the bus backed up and ran over me again, just for good measure, I'd presumed.

"Uh, yes, ma'am. I mean, no, ma'am. Nice to meet you, too." Naomi had told me a lot about her parents, but she hadn't prepared me for her mom's confusing welcome warning, all bundled into one. In time, Naomi's mother and I would come to be good friends, but I'd never have another greeting like that in all my life. It was one to remember! As the three of us chatted, I could tell Naomi's mom was sizing me up for her daughter. I hoped she liked me since I knew Naomi and her mom would most likely talk later, and I already knew how close they were and that Naomi valued her mom's opinion.

While her mother might have liked my dimples and found me to be a passable suitor for her daughter, Naomi's father's main interest was in Naomi's passing grades, and her grades weren't doing so well since she and I had started to date. She'd always been a good student, so it was clear, especially to her father, what Naomi's distraction was—me, the guy taking up his daughter's time and keeping her from her studies.

"He wants me to go to Hawaii to finish school out there," Naomi told me. "I don't really have a choice."

The news left me feeling gut-punched. I couldn't imagine losing my girl. What would I do without her? For all my life, I'd felt like I hadn't quite belonged, like I'd wanted to be in that inner circle, and being with Naomi had given me a sense of belonging. I liked how she and I fit together. I liked how I felt when we were we around each other. I couldn't imagine all that ending. As far as I was concerned, I had found the love of my life and I couldn't lose her. I would do what I had to in order to cement our relationship and look toward a future with Naomi in it.

Since all the important things in my life had seemed to take place at my home, the childhood home I'd always known, I knew where I'd do it. I bought the ring, thought about how I'd ask her, and then looked for just the right moment on the day we were together at my family's home on the lake. I asked her if she'd step over by the sliding glass doors for a minute.

As I held a long-stemmed rose toward Naomi, I looked hopefully into her eyes. "Nothing is as beautiful as you. Will you marry me?" That was when she saw the diamond engagement ring I'd slid onto the rose's long stem. Fortunately, she accepted the rose, the ring, and my marriage proposal. Relief washed over me. I had secured the girl and my future. Naomi would be mine after all, even though she'd go to Hawaii to finish school.

While I attended college in Washington, my fiancée studied over 2,500 miles away. The distance was tough, especially since Naomi and I only saw each other every six months for two weeks at a time. Maybe the unusual dynamics and the long-distance relationship were reasons she and I eventually quasi-dated others. Apart, we lived our own lives, surrounded by friends and having fun, but yet committed to one another both emotionally and sexually. We knew we were both young, and that marriage is a big commitment. Plus, it was no secret I'd smothered Naomi when we were together, my way of ensuring I'd win the pretty girl in the end. I probably didn't go about it the right way, but I hadn't had any examples of proper courtship, so I'd had to figure out the whole dating game as I went along, and even I knew I lacked some of the requisite skillsets.

When I was with Naomi, I wanted her badly. I didn't want to not have her in my life. Letting her go was difficult for me each time we had to part. Dating other girls just wasn't the answer. It wasn't what I wanted. I wanted Naomi, the cute girl in the long gray puffy coat I'd first laid eyes on and proclaimed would be my wife. I needed a firm commitment and I needed to move forward with the next step in my life.

"Listen, Naomi," I said after a couple of years, "you need to go ahead and marry me, or you need to let me go."

Even getting words out had been difficult. I wanted her answer, but I knew I risked a reply I might not like to hear. Yet I couldn't take any more of the highs and lows of our relationship. It had worn on me for too long. As she thought about my ultimatum, I held my breath and waited to learn how my life would play out.

"Okay, let's do it."

I finally exhaled, relieved I wouldn't have to grieve the loss of the girl I really wanted to marry. My heart had been spared. Life would go on. I could begin the next phase of my adult life.

We got married in July of 1990. Since all the important life events took place on the lake I'd always loved, our wedding was at the home of my parents' neighbors, and our reception was on my parents' lakefront lawn. Our wedding day was momentous for me, and for many reasons. I began my new life with Naomi, the woman who would be my wife, my life partner, and the mother of my children.

In addition to my parents, Irene, my childhood nanny, was at our wedding. It felt as if life had come full-circle when my eyes met Irene's. She'd been like a second mother to me, that extra-special woman in my childhood who'd had such a profound importance in my life. The day wouldn't have been the same had she not been there to watch me marry Naomi. I'd always been an emotional guy, so Irene wasn't at all surprised by my tears as we hugged. She had always understood me, even without a single word being spoken.

CHAPTER 4

LIFE BEGINS

Naomi and I moved into a small condo and began life as newly-weds. It's probably only natural that people frame their ideals about marriage from their own experiences and what they've seen in their lives. Naomi had told me all about her dad, a successful accountant and ladies' man, and how his actions had impacted her. She had watched her father's philandering behavior and its impact on her mother. She'd also felt the pain and angst of being a child from a broken home, torn apart by divorce, when her mother had finally had enough of her dad's cheating ways.

"I won't be like my mom, not ever!" Naomi proclaimed. "Their divorce shattered my sister and me."

Those words and Naomi's forthright tone would come back to me in years to come. But when she'd first told me, I had felt sorry she'd had to go through the pain and disappointment that blanketed her family. I wondered if she had predisposed notions about men and cheating, or if she thought most men were like her father. One thing was sure: I liked Naomi's dedication to her marriage and to the family she and I would one day have together. My wife was a solid woman with unwavering, steadfast values, and she put others first. Even then, I knew Naomi was special.

We spent the first five years of our marriage just getting to know each other, learning to live together, and bonding. Those were good days, when we were young and just starting out. I worked as a salesperson in our family business, and I was really good at my job, something that brought me pride and fulfillment. Naomi worked as a receptionist at a local hair salon. She didn't enjoy being in the spotlight; she always liked to be in the background, the one quietly in control, steering things and making progress happen.

When Naomi and I learned she was pregnant, we were both thrilled. We'd already had five years together, just the two of us, so we were ready to share our life with a child of our own. Since our apartment was too small, we bought a cute three-bedroom home, and Naomi got busy decorating it and turning it into a home for us. Our son arrived and lit up our world. Nothing could have been better, not for either one of us. Naomi and I had discussed that she'd stay home and raise our kids and I would be the main breadwinner. That was our plan.

For a while, Naomi and I fell into that typical routine all parents know. It was a repetitive cycle of work, home, sleep, repeat; and as I was able, I did Daddy Duty. Our family business was doing very well, but my dad was now sixty-five and talking about retiring. He wanted to slow down and simplify his life.

"So, Dad," I said one day, "what are you going to do with the lake house?"

"Why do you ask?"

"Well, you know I've always loved that house with its views of Mount Rainier and how it sits on the lake. I've always thought I'd like to raise my own kids in the house and let them have the same experiences I had as a kid. I'd love for them to grow up on the lake and be with the baby ducks and smell the seasons change, just like I did."

Dad thought about it for a minute and then said, "Tell you what, you can pay all the carrying expenses for the house and you can live there."

I was elated by Dad's offer. Naomi and I could handle paying the taxes, insurance, upkeep, and various expenses, and I'd be back on the lake I had always loved so much. I looked forward to fishing with my own son on the lake, just like Dad had fished with me.

Moving into one's parents' home is an unusual feeling. Sure, I'd grown up in that house, but now I went back as a grown man, a husband and a father. I was now the man of the house, no longer the little boy, the outcast youngest sibling who never seemed to fit into my own family. The house still smelled the same; it even looked the same. Even the ghosts of the past were still in that house, some comforting, others not so much. It had been the last place my sister had taken a breath, but that brought some comfort since she was still within its walls. Even my older brother, who'd become an emancipated teenager and fled our father's domineering wrath, was somehow still in that house with us. But sleeping in the master bedroom with Naomi, on that first night, was really odd. I had to get used to the fact that it was our bedroom, not Mom and Dad's room anymore.

Along with the memories that crowded me in the house were tons of "stuff" Mom and Dad had stored in the house and garage. I couldn't say anything since they'd allowed us to move in and only pay the expenses of the home. But once we'd moved in with all our stuff, on top of Mom and Dad's stuff, there was quite a bit of stuff in that lake house! To make matters worse, I was a guy who enjoyed my toys. As I began to make a little money, I enjoyed occasionally rewarding myself with a new toy in the form of a watercraft or Jet Ski, the newest electronics, the fanciest gadgets that had just come out, or whatever I felt like. I had that guys' mentality that whoever dies with the most toys, wins. But my garage was only so big, and what I couldn't purchase was stress relief or a quick fix for the increasing anxiety that welled within me. It would be years before I'd get a reality check and figure out that things don't make us happy and complete. At the time, I was still bogged down in the rat race and working to buy more and better things to add to my life. I thought that was the game and the goal. I didn't realize how it was causing me so much stress and inner turmoil.

My mom's decorating tastes had always leaned toward beige. We'd always had beige, beige, and more, beige. If Mom wanted to live a little, she used a *patterned* beige, but it was always beige. The monochromatic color could have been Mom's attempt at keeping Dad calm. Whatever her reasoning, the beige had to go. Room by room, I redid our home and brought in some color and pattern. Maybe it was also my way of pushing out some old memories and making room for new ones.

The days were long, and the nights of sleep were too short and too few. At first, the routine didn't bother me. I didn't even notice it so much. But the grind caught up with me. I went to work and put in super-long days, went home and ate a late dinner, sometimes had sex with Naomi, and then fell into bed, depleted and exhausted. When the alarm rang, the whole predictable routine started all over again. I began to wonder if that was all there was to life for me. In those days, I wasn't thinking of Naomi or of how hard she had it as a stay-at-home, full-time mom with our son. Years would pass before

I'd acknowledge that while I went to work, she did the hardest job on the planet.

At the time, I was caught up in my own issues and thinking about all that was going on within myself. In my last year of college, I'd been diagnosed with type 2 diabetes, also known at the time as adult-onset diabetes. It was daunting to know no cure existed for the disease and I had to think about everything I ate and everything I did. The doctor explained to me that at just age twenty-three, I presented with the symptoms of a seventy-year-old man. Peripheral neuropathy was causing my nerves to die; I got diabetic ulcers in my feet that could require surgery; I could later require bone removal; I could even one day require amputation, due to infection. Not only would all that be costly, inconvenient, and painful, but it would limit what I could do with my life. The whole "what if" scenario was what really got to me, I think. As I'd done during my childhood, I often reached for food to comfort me when I felt stressed or upset. This new revelation had only made matters worse.

Comfort food as a coping mechanism became a part of my regular routine—and so did my subsequent steady weight gain. When Naomi got pregnant again, I thought seriously about how I needed to get a handle on my health so I'd be around for my wife and kids. But with just the same twenty-four hours in a day, I was in a rut and my routine had swallowed me whole. When we welcomed our baby daughter into the world, Naomi had her hands fuller than ever while I worked in the family business. The years flew by before either one of us knew it.

By the time our daughter was eight, Naomi had organized a father-dance. While I was proud to escort our daughter to the dance, I was thoroughly disgusted with myself. At 355 pounds, I weighed ninety pounds more than when I had graduated high school. My health was at risk and so was my life. Clothes didn't fit right. Hell, my skin didn't even feel like it fit right! I felt gigantic and I hated myself. It was also hard to feel good about myself in my clunky, dorky "Herman Munster" shoes I wore, thanks to my diabetes. I had nothing going for myself in the sex department either; any of the sporadic, kinky stuff was entirely out of the question for a guy my size who easily got winded.

One day, as I looked out over the serene lake in our yard, I regretted that I couldn't go into the lake with our kids. With the open sores on my feet that resisted healing, I couldn't risk getting my feet wet for fear of potential infection. I had wanted so badly to live on the lake so my kids could have the experiences I'd had as a kid, yet I couldn't do the things with them that I had done. We had all the toys, all the fishing gear, and the Jet Skis, yet I couldn't use them with our kids. It wasn't fair, none of it. I was cheating my children of the experiences and memories we could be making. I was cheating Naomi of her husband. I was cheating myself of *life*. I couldn't allow myself to diminish further and eventually become a gross, dependent, wound-care patient, relegated to the life of being cared for by others like some useless slug that just exists and waits to die. That's just not who I was meant to be. Deep down, I knew that was not me, not at all.

A shift was happening within me as I started to evaluate the time I had left in this world, and it felt like I didn't have long. I was sure of it. I felt it. My health wasn't good. I wasn't taking care of myself. I looked like absolute hell. Let's be honest; I felt like a ticking time bomb. I'd always been a no-nonsense, forthright guy when it came to business. Respectful, but to the point, I'd roll over people to get what I wanted. I'd found it was what always worked for me. When I thought of my take-charge demeanor in business, a lightbulb went on. Infection had nearly killed me twice before, my weight was grossly out of control, and I wasn't living life to the fullest. I wasn't even enjoying living or getting up in the morning. But whose fault was it, *any of it?*

"I'm not living like this anymore," I ultimately decided. "I have a choice, damn it!"

It boiled down to taking responsibility and making choices. In life, we all have choices. What we do with those choices decides so much about our outcomes, and choices give us control. When people complain about their circumstances, as if they've had no hand in where they are, it is so limiting. It's also, in my opinion, pretty pathetic. But the moment they take responsibility, they also take control. That's an approach I respect! Sure, we might not always make the correct choices, but the wrong choice is better than being stagnant and making no choice at all. Still today, one of my biggest pet peeves is people who blame others for *their* life failures. On the other hand, I have great deference for those who take personal responsibility, even for gigantic failures, because it shows they are in control, making decisions, and grabbing life. Those are the people to be commended. As a kid, I'd watched my dad do it, and while some might say he hadn't been the perfect example of a father all the time, he did provide some valuable examples and life lessons.

Once I'd made the decision to take control and lose the weight, a shift started to take place within me. Making the choice and taking control put me in charge, in a power position, and I liked the feeling. I took personal responsibility for my health, my physical appearance, my energy level, and even the amount of gratification I was finding in my sex life. One thing I had going for me was that when I made up my mind to do something, I focused on it, worked toward it, and made it to my goal. Losing the weight wasn't easy, but seeing it come off was fulfilling, and that kept me going. Little by little, as I buckled my belt in the next, tighter hole, I got closer and closer to my goal. As the numbers on the scale decreased, I vowed never again to allow myself to balloon to an unhealthy weight.

When I first decided to lose the weight, I hadn't expected everything that would follow. My initial objective had been much simpler than what would come later. Yet in losing the weight, something amazing happened because I found *myself* under all that weight. Alexander D. Banks began to emerge, but even I would have to get to know the man I met in the mirror each morning. I had to admit the guy was looking better. He even carried himself differently, more confidently, shoulders back as he strode into the room in his new svelte form.

But there was still a divide between Naomi and me, and it was the size of the Grand Canyon. It felt like if I tried to holler at her from one side of the massive chasm, she'd never hear me as she busied herself, lost in her own world. She wouldn't even see me, let alone hear me. Her nights were spent upstairs alone as she thumb-fucked her iPad and watched *Dancing with the Stars*. The separation between us was so much bigger than just the two stories in our home. I wanted more. No, I needed more. I craved more.

Since the beginning of time, it's been no secret that of the two sexes, men are the hunters. When we need something, we will find it. But when I first sat down at my computer, in the downstairs in our home, it wasn't my intention to set off on the journey that would begin. I had no idea, in fact, what I was doing or where life might lead me. All I knew was I needed to feel valued and I had to find an escape from the mundane monotony of my ho-hum life. It wasn't that I did not love Naomi. It never was about that specific emotion. It had to do with what I needed for me, for Alex, to feed my soul, and when a man is hungry, he will find food and he will eat. It is a basic raw survival instinct.

Now, I was also a great salesman and a top-notch businessman, but this was entirely different. I'd been a married guy all of my adult life. I had no clue how to go about talking to women. Thankfully, the computer made it easier and safer. Sitting in the comfort of my own home, I felt brazen as I surfed the Web and found the options were endless. Blondes, brunettes, and redheads abounded! Tall, short, thin, thick, Caucasian, Latina, every ethnicity, shape, and size imaginable! I soon realized that being online and looking at the various options of women was very similar to catalog shopping, or even scrolling through Amazon pages as I perused the endless options. Who knew it was so easy to connect with the opposite sex? I'd been buried in work and bogged down in responsibility for so long I'd had no idea how far things had come. Then I found this jackpot site called Tinder! What a concept! One could virtually see the interminable selections of hot, horny women ready to meet and drop their panties! As I read the women's bios, I grew increasingly intrigued. Of course, I realized some of the women might not be entirely truthful. After all, the ladies' goal was to get men to call them. I had written ad copy before, and I'd surely paid for plenty of advertising in my years in business, so I got the drill. Plus, a few of the photos appeared to have been edited or altered.

As I scrolled through the pages, smiling ladies stared back at me, some scantily clad, while others looked like typical moms in the carpool line at school. One was dressed in a skimpy nurse's costume. She reminded me of the time when I'd had a brief month-long fling with a real nurse. It had happened when I'd felt so unattractive and down on myself. She had shown an interest in me when even I wasn't interested in myself. But I had been careless by haphazardly leaving my computer on one day, so Naomi had seen an email the nurse had sent to me. Our life had been so chaotic at the time that Naomi had taken some of the blame for not putting more effort into our marriage. She was actually more vengeful toward the nurse than toward me.

At this time, I came to understand my love language was through touch but Naomi's was through acts of service. I had needed attention and physical touch, while Naomi had needed help around the house for her to feel loved. I had been so unhappy then—at a breaking point, overweight, miserable, lonely, and desperate for more out of my life—that I had eagerly accepted that nurse's attentions. But my self-esteem really suffered, and I hurt Naomi, too. Worse still, I didn't solve anything since I still craved something to feed that hunger inside of me that I still could not identify.

I guess I was still searching to find something in myself. I was seeking answers. Why I thought I'd find them on Tinder, I don't know. What I found were countless hot, horny women, all of whom had the same burning desires to be heard and to have their needs met. There were corporate executives, housewives, mothers, married women, single women…you name it; I met their demographic on Tinder. In time, after I had exchanged a few online messages with some of the women, we then shared emails with more details of ourselves. That progressed to phone calls. I heard in several women's voices a quiet desperation to be heard and to have their desires met. I listened to them, really listened to them, even to how they breathed as we spoke. One night, when I was sure Naomi was fast asleep, I locked my office door and spoke quietly in my phone to one woman. "Go ahead and remove your panties," I told her. At first, she laughed. When I repeated myself, she seemed almost relieved to obey. "Take off your shirt now," I instructed, "and your bra." She giggled for a moment, but I said, "Listen, you're all by yourself; it's fine. Turn off the lamp and lie down. Just listen to my voice." Slowly, but firmly, I instructed her to touch herself and not to stop. At first, she talked to me. But when she stopped talking back to me, I just listened and continued to coach her—all the way through climax.

"Oh, my God," she sighed. "Can you call me back tomorrow night, same time?"

· · ·

I was a middle-aged guy who loved his wife, but who felt entirely invisible around her. In 2015, after Naomi discovered my fling with the nurse, it had to stop. She was quiet about my infidelity for a while. Over and over again, I remembered she had said she'd never do to our kids what her parents' divorce had done to her sister and her. Naomi had always been such a good mother. There was no denying it. She'd always put our kids first. I could never fault her in that department.

Our son was a great kid. In fact, we'd recently allowed him to move his girlfriend into our home after she'd had a falling out with her own parents—or, at least, that was what she'd told us, maybe so we'd feel sorry for her; we couldn't be sure. Naomi and I had wanted to keep our kids close. Family was so important to us. Our daughter was a fiery redhead who'd always spoken her mind and could take care of herself in most situations. We were proud of the young woman she was becoming. Neither Naomi nor I wanted to rock that boat or stall her life's progress. She was a little dynamo in the making who'd be off to college soon. If there was one thing Naomi and I had gotten right, it was our kids. Although my affair had hurt

Naomi, I deeply respected her strength and steadfast conviction to put our family first and carry on for the sake of the kids. Their best interest was what mattered to her.

In addition to having our son's girlfriend living with us, there were always additional upheavals, unusual circumstances, and stressors in our home. As I said before, we physically had accumulated so much stuff that it felt as if we were literally bursting at the seams. I'd always thought we were supposed to work hard so we could buy all the latest gadgets, gizmos, electronics, vehicles, and toys. But all those things must be stored somewhere, and although our home had a decent amount of square footage, Mom and Dad still kept a lot of their stuff in it, too. Maybe it was easy for me to get lost amid all the stuff and to feel invisible in my own home with my wife.

As my parents' faithful "go-to son," I was the one who regularly flew to Arizona, at a moment's notice, to be there for them, to check on them, do house repairs, or do whatever they might need. My siblings were unconcerned with our parents. Caring for Mom and Dad was a self-imposed duty, but it added to my stressors and obligations, and the pressure only grew. One day, as I flew down, I envisioned how easy it would be if I had a pressure-relief valve, a simple release I could open to let go of some of the stress that had built up inside of me like a pressure cooker whose lid was threatening to blow off. I chuckled to myself since most men know right where our valve is located, don't we? Simple fix, right, gentlemen?

I witnessed my dad's decline since I saw him more often than the others. He and Mom had lived such an orderly and predictable life for all of their marriage. They were so old-school. It had always been cocktails until 6:00 p.m., followed by dinner. Life for them was neat and tidy, just how they'd liked it, with no surprises to rock their boat. Everything had been scheduled in their lives, but there were some things even Mom and Dad couldn't control. Their aging health was one of them. Mom and Dad made the decision to "move up," back into the family house with us. Naomi flew down to help them pack up their things, ending their dreams of retirement and moving them back into their home, again, asserting to us it was their home—adding to the pressure still. Turning up the heat of the pressure cooker at home eventually made life so uncomfortable that my son decided at eighteen to move out of the home I thought was ours and fracture my family. As I look back, his decision was the right one to make. Dad died a year later.

After Naomi and I survived my fling with the nurse, I lost my dad. Needless to say, it was up to me to help Mom with Dad's estate, and I continued to help her after my dad had died. While I was able to bring order to Dad's estate, there was one thing I couldn't do: I couldn't assuage my guilt that I wasn't with Dad when he died. It would be one of my biggest regrets and something that would forever plague me. Add *that* to the growing baggage I carried, and it seemed like my knuckles should be dragging on the ground like an ape's.

CHAPTER 5

CROWDED HOUSE

I've heard it said that the death of a parent is a major life-changing, pivotal time. Perhaps it's true. Maybe the same things would have happened anyway, yet I'll never know. But with Dad gone, Mom needed a lot of help from me, understandably, and I still had the pressure of my business, the stress at home, and an overwhelming hunger in my gut that gnawed at me all the time. Naomi seemed content to keep going along, just as things were, but I needed to shake things up a bit, find some excitement, and see what else life might have to offer.

Questions crept into my thoughts as I considered my options. Was it a midlife crisis? Was my clock ticking? Had I begun to think of my own mortality even more because I'd lost my dad? Was I feeling good about myself for the first time in my life and wanted to be appreciated by the opposite sex? Was I just a guy who craved some good, exciting sex, beyond the vanilla, predictable sex I'd known?

I had always hated when Naomi said, "Shh! Someone might hear!" when we'd been making love. "We're in our own house!" I'd always remind her. "We *are* married!" But the mood was inevitably gone, and Naomi always said, "Right, but my mom is down the hall!" Naomi's mom and I had become great friends, but when she'd come to live with us, I had never expected that putting her in-residence would be at the expense of my sex life. I was pretty sure our son and his girlfriend had a much better sex life than Naomi and I did—in *my* house! There was something very wrong with the whole scenario.

Mom's health had begun to deteriorate also. First, she required knee surgery, and then she was diagnosed with uterine cancer. Like always, Mom's care fell to me, and she was a handful because I swear the woman had the pain tolerance of a gnat. With Dad gone, everything Mom needed fell on my shoulders.

Years earlier, Mom had tried to assert her dominance by tossing around comments like, "I wonder what we might get for this house if we were to put it on the market?" It was her way of reminding us that we were in her house. I never liked how she'd done that, but I had tried to put away my feelings of resentment and remember she was my mother. One thing was for sure, my kids had witnessed their family stick together and help their elders. I felt good that we'd taught them values and had given them a foundation on which to build their lives—even *if* Mom's comments had been like nails on a chalkboard to my ears.

Having Mom and Naomi under one roof was like having two queens trying to rule a kingdom. Each woman thought she should be in charge, and each looked to me as if I should be the tiebreaker or referee. That was not a position any man would envy. Mom felt like she was the older woman and it was her house, so *she* should be in charge. Naomi felt like she was my wife and our kids' mother, so *she* had the final word.

"Alex, there's nothing more we can do for your mom," her doctor told me after he'd motioned me out into the hall from her exam room. "I can give you more pain pills and make her comfortable, but that's all."

I had known we were near the end for some time. It was no secret to anyone that Mom had been willing herself to die. She was ready to go. Since I had to be at the store, I immediately looked for a private care home for my mom. But she wasn't at the home for long. Ten days after the doctor talked to me, Mom was gone. The worst part was I wasn't with her when she died. I missed saying goodbye by just fifteen minutes. Once again, an ocean of guilt washed over me. Mom had left me, and I didn't get to hold her hand and tell her I loved her just one last time. What kind of son was I?

· · ·

Naomi's and my sex life had become nonexistent, but after Mom died, a bit of pressure was off me and our home only had one queen in it. I was hopeful our marriage and sex life would improve. But Naomi and I still had a few of those underlying, nagging old arguments that couples never resolve, but simply put away, those issues that can't be discussed without erupting into ugliness. For instance, although Naomi's mom had lived with us and been great at staying out of our personal business, she had once made a small loan to me for the down-payment on our first little home. Long story short, when the property appreciated, she wanted to realize the property's appreciation after appraisal, so she wanted me to pay her my equity when we sold the house, instead of just being paid back the amount of the original loan.

"Who does that?" I'd asked Naomi. "Is the woman a loan shark?"

But Naomi defiantly took her mother's side, for whatever reason, and I felt betrayed. It drove a wedge between us, as money matters often do with relationships. I'd always liked Naomi's mom, and I'd liked that she'd been there for Naomi, even during our arguments, but this had crossed the line of family bounds. Money and family often don't mix, as I was learning. Even after Mom had died, I inherited one of my parents' commercial properties, while my brother inherited another property. While it had seemed fair to our parents, my brother resented that I also got the lake house, even though he had never expressed the least bit of interest in the family home we'd grown up in. It was one of those issues we'd never resolve, yet an underlying bone of contention.

. . .

When Mom had been in pain from the cancer, I had sought relief for her in the form of marijuana edibles, legal in our state, but just coming out at the time. It was then I met Lacey through Craigslist where she advertised that she sold the edibles. A bit younger than I, Lacey was also a gourmet cook, and she baked the best lemon bars I'd ever tasted. But it wasn't Lacey's finesse in the kitchen that got my attention. Sure, my mouth literally watered for her lemon bars, but blue-eyed Lacey had more than culinary talents. She came into my life at a time when I was just feeling the first bit of freedom after having been weighed down for all of my life by others' expectations. I felt it my responsibility to live up to my parents' hopes and dreams for me, never mind what I wanted. Especially when it came to Mom, I'd felt that, in some way, if I'd aspired to be what she'd dreamt for me, that her pain over losing Krissy would somehow be less. I'd made it my mission to find out what Mom thought I should do, be, think, and even feel, and then deliver it. But decades had passed, and I had missed out on so much. I hadn't done so much of what I wanted to do!

Worse still, since I'd worked in our family-owned business, it had been difficult for me to measure my own value and worth. Sure, it was undeniable that I was a stellar salesman. The numbers proved it. But how did I compare, as a guy, a solo man, an individual? When one works in his family's business, he's got to work so much harder just so it doesn't appear that his success was handed to him. I'd been throwing myself into our business for years to make sure I made an impact and an impression that was beyond reproach. No one would look at me and say I hadn't worked for what I had—even if it nearly killed me. Yet the long hours, the lack of intimacy with Naomi, the stress, and overall disconnect in life, was catching up with me.

"Talk to me; tell me about your day," Lacey said one day when I went by to visit her after Mom had died. I had to look behind myself for a minute, just to see if someone else was standing there. Was the bright-eyed dishwater-blonde talking to me? Did she just invite me to share my thoughts and feelings? Had she just opened the door for me to connect with her? I was not used to such attention, especially since Naomi had been especially busy lately with her job as an executive secretary for a local college.

It sounds cliché, but it began innocently enough, with friendly conversation. Lacey listened, really listened. Better still, she then asked questions and invited additional input. Suddenly, I felt eight-feet tall and like the star quarterback as the hottest cheerleader pursued me! When Lacey suggested we could go into the bedroom and continue our conversation, I'm pretty sure I levitated across the floor. My wife wasn't giving me the time of day, but I had Lacey's full attention and the feeling was intoxicating. Before long, the only thing Lacey wore was the single diamond stud in her nose.

"Ever use one of these?" she asked as she held a rod-like handle with long leather tails.

Lacey introduced me to the lifestyle that would bring me a step closer to knowing the real me, the guy I'd been born to be. She allowed me to tie her to her bed and flog her that day, followed by great sex. The metamorphosis could not be stopped, nor would I want it to be. For the first time, I'd found the most intense sense of satisfaction, freedom, and gratification, all rolled into one, as if I'd finally found the equilibrium I'd been seeking in my life. Relief flooded over me and a renewed sense of peace filled me because my eyes had been opened to the possibilities of what great BDSM sex could be and of who I could be in this life.

Yet my very proper wife was not going to have it, not for one minute. So, I kept Lacey a secret and met her regularly for our clandestine trysts. I thought Naomi eyed me with skepticism a few times. Did she know? Had she suspected something? Surely, she wasn't missing the sex between us since it had been nonexistent anyway. I didn't have a plan for how I'd proceed. All I knew was I enjoyed dominating Lacey, and she clearly loved it, too.

While things were looking up with me, life at home was getting even worse. As the calendar pages flipped in 2016, tension mounted, and it seemed as if everything I did irritated Naomi. I thought maybe a vacation might help things, just a getaway to new surroundings where we'd be away from the daily stresses.

"Let's take that trip to Alaska," I suggested one night.

"The promo trip you won through the business just before your mom died?" Naomi asked.

"Yeah, let's go to Alaska, just the two of us. What do you think?"

"You know I can only take time off in July! How come you can never seem to remember that?"

It was true. With her job, she could only take vacation time in July. But I'd thought she might still be able at least to ask for the time off. She didn't see it that way, however. Instead, she suggested I take our daughter on the trip. But when our daughter had accompanied me on another trip to Vegas, she'd done nothing but whine about heat, the crowds, and almost everything else. I couldn't imagine being in Alaska with a complaining teenage girl while we were surrounded by pristine, majestic scenery.

Life with Naomi moved on as predictably as ever as she and I went to our respective jobs each day, separate from one another, came home, and still went in two, different directions. I began to wonder just how many episodes of *Dancing with the Stars* my wife could watch. Yet Naomi seemed satisfied with our bland, boring, ho-hum life. One night, after I'd gotten home late from the store and eaten dinner, I went and logged on to Tinder. By this point, I was no longer just curiously surfing; I felt like an old pro. I was seeing Lacey regularly, and I felt great about myself, both as a man and as a Dom. I enjoyed just knowing I identified as a dominant in the BDSM community. There was great, heady power in that, and I owned it.

On this night, I took the next step by creating a profile for myself. I smiled as I typed the words: ***I'm a Dom man, going through a divorce***. In no time, I was immersed in conversation with six women and having a ball. Meanwhile, Naomi was upstairs listening to Claudio or Bruno or whoever pontificate about some guy's ability to anticipate his partner's next step in the cha-cha.

One woman, Brooke, typed a question to me: "Is that a Dom with a capital or a lowercase *D*?"

I liked her already. I laughed as I replied, "Oh, that's a *CAPITAL* D!"

I had always been a chameleon, that guy who could blend in with any type of crowd, and bend and morph to fit the occasion or the circumstance. I'd always figured it was part of what made me such a great salesman. I could talk to anyone, find a commonality with every person I met, and make him or her feel entirely at ease. Within minutes, it was like we were old friends. Yet I wasn't faking it; I really liked talking with people and getting to know them, finding out what made them tick. It was my communication style and also my management style with my business. I'd always been clear and direct with people. There was no gray area. People always knew where I stood. It saved time, something I particularly liked.

So, as I typed my replies online to the ladies, I was direct and friendly as we chatted, just as I'd have been if we'd met in person. Brooke really resonated with me. There was something about her that stood out to me. She had piqued my curiosity more than just a little. Her face on her Tinder profile was cute, but I couldn't be sure whether she'd posted an older photo since I knew many people, especially women, seemed to favor sharing younger, thinner, more flattering pictures of themselves on their profiles. She appeared to me to be a typical mom-type with a friendly face and nice smile. I liked her energy and attitude and wanted to know more about her, so I asked if she'd like to meet for coffee. Sure, I was crossing the proverbial line, but it felt like my wife had long-since forgotten about me and entirely lost interest in our sex life. It felt like the only way to get Naomi's attention again would be to dance in the finals on *Dancing with the Stars*, and I wasn't willing to go that route. (Besides, I didn't think my Herman Munster shoes would be the best choice for the TV dance floor.) Coffee with Brooke seemed easier, and like it might produce quicker, more favorable results. As a businessman, I was looking for the fastest ROI, after all.

We met at a Starbucks halfway between our homes. I had no feelings of guilt nor any remorse. I was simply focused on filling that void inside of me, that need to be appreciated, valued, and "seen" again. While my conscience didn't weigh heavily on me, my nerves did. As I drove closer to the rendezvous point, my heart raced with anticipation, almost like a teenager on his first date. At this time, I was still about forty pounds overweight, but I'd begun to work on myself and had made progress.

As soon as I arrived, I recognized Brooke from her photo. We said hello and then sat and talked over coffee. Her appearance made me feel more at ease since she looked like the typical, generic, mother who doesn't necessarily stand out among the crowd, though at the same time, she was nice-looking enough. Let's face it, if she'd been a sexy, hot-to-trot hard-body, I would have been so intimidated I'd have felt out of my league. As we talked and got to know each other, I decided I liked Brooke.

"I really like your personality," I told her. She smiled over her coffee before she sipped it, without taking her eyes off me.

We both felt it—that fiery electricity that zapped and danced between us. An invisible magnetic pull drew us to one another. I'd been nervous, just a little while earlier, uncomfortable in my own skin, but this friendly, smiling woman had dissolved my nerves and replaced them with a newfound confidence. My shoulders had relaxed, and I sat taller than before. I liked how I felt when I was with this woman. There was a stirring within me, something more than sexual, that I couldn't quite explain. It was like a combustion had taken place, and I knew I didn't want the flickering heat inside me to go out again.

"Would you like to meet again?" I asked Brooke hopefully, as we walked out of Starbucks a while later.

"Sure! Definitely." She smiled up at me.

"I'll give you a call then, and we can grab some lunch."

"Perfect."

I was still seeing Lacey at the time, and now I had new possibilities on the horizon with Brooke. I knew Brooke had felt the sparks between us, just as I did. They'd been undeniable; it felt like a soul entangling existed between us as if we were soulmates. The hunger in me was only growing. I couldn't wait long to make a lunch date with Brooke. Just knowing she waited for me had made me crave her, yet I was still shocked that she'd found me attractive, especially when I didn't like the man who stared back at me from the mirror. I couldn't understand it, but I was no fool, and I wasn't about to waste a great opportunity.

Brooke and I met again, this time over lunch as we'd planned. When the waitress brought our menus, it wasn't food that had my mouth salivating. In fact, my nerves were so frayed I was sure I wouldn't be able to eat when our lunches arrived. Brooke and I made polite, friendly conversation. I felt as if I might be all at once pulled by that powerful, invisible force, across the tabletop to the woman with the coquettish eyes. She continued to lick her lips with her exquisite pink tongue as she spoke. I repositioned myself in my seat to accommodate the growing appreciation inside my pants. Brooke's cheeks, neck, and cleavage were rosy. I knew she was warm and eager, just as I was, but we both seemed to know we needed to hold back and respect some unwritten protocol that no physical interaction could take place until the next date. As she spoke, my mind drifted off. I imagined raking off all the dishes and glassware and taking her right there on top of our table.

"You know what I mean?" she asked.

"Oh, uh, I'm sorry. I didn't catch that last part."

Instead of repeating herself, Brooke laughed, buttered a roll, placed it on my bread plate, and then did the same for herself. The waiter soon brought our entrées, but I wasn't interested in the food, not in the slightest; nor was she. I made myself eat, just to be polite, as Brooke told me more about herself.

"And I left home at seventeen," she went on, "and headed to Vegas. With no real skillsets, I worked in a mediocre office job and dabbled as a call girl once in a while to make ends meet for a year. But I guess I wasn't very good at it."

She threw her head back and laughed at the memory, so I did the same. But I was curious to hear more. She went on to explain that since being a sex worker wasn't paying the bills, she had decided she needed another plan. That meant some schooling was in order.

"I knew I had to focus on my education. I got my therapist's degree."

"Well, that explains it," I said, winking. "I'm always attracted to smart women."

"Yeah, well, maybe not as smart as some might think. I got pregnant by a guy I didn't even know. Not the brightest move, but my son is the best thing in my life."

Her eyes lit up when she spoke of her son. It was obvious she was a mother who cared deeply for her boy. The puzzle pieces had begun to fall into place as I learned more about the woman before me.

"Wow, so you were a single mother?" I asked. "That had to be a feat."

"I did what I had to do. It wasn't like I had much of choice, really."

As she spoke, I watched her lips move and I wondered what they felt like, what they tasted like. She and I were alone in our own little world, secluded from reality and the trappings and stresses of the day-to-day. We'd created our private, ensconced haven, safe from the realism that brought us stress, angst, and worries. We could be who and what we wanted. The opportunities were endless, and I know now that was part of what titillated both of us. I craved escapism from my monotonous, vanilla life, and Brooke just happened to be the woman sitting in front of me, feeding my ravenous ego. But there's not a man alive, none I've met anyway, who will not find food when he needs to eat. Since the beginning of time, man has gone to the ends of the Earth to find his fill and quell that hungry beast inside, and the food on my plate was not feeding my hunger, not in the least. On one hand, I didn't want to end our date. On the other, I wanted to leave so I could make another date with her and take things to the next level as quickly as possible.

When we said our goodbyes, it was with the understanding that we'd meet again soon. We both knew what would happen. It was clear we both wanted it. I can't even say I was led astray or had no idea what was happening. I did. I knew. I even had Brooke's number. I knew what she was and what she wanted from me.

Blondish and in her mid-forties, Brooke was smart, I'll give her that. But she thought she was smarter than everyone else around her, myself included. At first, I found her tantalizing and wanted to see where things might go with us. I mean, Naomi wasn't exactly interested in me anymore; she all but ignored my presence each night when I came home. My wife had her life and I had mine. It felt like life had passed me by, and the clock was ticking. If I wanted to experience life, it was up to me to see what else was out there. Some might call it a midlife crisis, but I can't label it. I just looked back at the past decades and realized I hadn't had enough fun in my life.

My two best guy friends had told me about their younger years. I hadn't done all the crazy things they'd done. Some might say I married too young and shouldn't have settled down with Naomi when I did. But I hadn't wanted to lose her, and at the time, it had seemed like the right choice. But when I'd hit midlife, I had looked back and thought about all the things I hadn't done for myself, for Alex. Was it selfish? Perhaps. But is that so bad? We only get one life, just one lifetime to really experience all the things we want to do, and then it's all over. I couldn't waste any more time pontificating on the morality of it. That damned clock was ticking, and let's be honest, my health wasn't exactly so great. Every time I looked down at my feet, those telltale Herman Munster shoes reminded me I was a diabetic and life could change for me in an instant.

CHAPTER 6

THE OTHER WOMAN

It wasn't my black Herman Munster shoes I was thinking of the day I drove to meet Brooke for our next lunch date. It was the twinkle in her eyes and her luscious, moist lips. When I turned my crew-cab pickup truck into the restaurant's parking lot and parked beside her car, I knew she was already inside waiting for me, as eager to see me as I was to meet her again. It felt good to know she was early and anticipating seeing me. It was great to be needed and wanted by a woman.

Our second lunch was just like the first, and the sexual energy between us was constant. It was so heavy I could have sworn it was visible to the other diners. Brooke traced my fingers with her fingertips as she talked, and I thought I might jump across the table to get to her. When our food came, I didn't even want to eat it. All I wanted was to touch her and feel her skin. But I wasn't exactly practiced in the art of dating or how to do these things. So I held back and continued to make polite conversation.

"Tell me more about your son," I said with as much restraint as I could manage.

"He's been such a light in my life," she beamed, "an Eagle Scout, just a really great kid. I was a den mother when he was younger."

"I'll bet the fathers hit on you."

"Oh, I dated my share of weirdos and dweebs," she laughed. "Trust me, I've had some real winners."

"What do you mean?"

"It's been hard to find a man, a real man, I mean. I can't find a man who can handle me in bed. Most men just really suck."

I was interested, very interested. Challenge accepted.

"Well, my first rule with women is that the woman must orgasm first, and then I get to do whatever I want," I explained.

"I like that!"

As we ate, the conversation got even more sexual. The topic of cucumbers came up, at first, as a joke.

"Oh, I'd do that!" Brooke offered. "Should I bring one or two?"

"Definitely two!"

I liked her even better, I decided. She had my full attention by the time the check came. I couldn't pay the waiter fast enough, and I told him to keep the change. Brooke and I walked out of the restaurant and toward my truck, which was parked in the rear of the lot behind the restaurant. As I went to kiss her, she returned my kiss, hot and heavy. In no time, we were in the backseat of my truck and the windows were completely fogged-up. She was all the dessert I needed that afternoon.

"When can I see you again?" I asked.

"I like your confidence!" she laughed.

"I usually get what I want!"

"I can tell!"

We both knew something was beginning between us, but we had no idea where it might take us. When I left her that day, I felt like a college kid. I couldn't get her off my mind and felt like I was walking on air. It felt so good to be needed, to be wanted, to be desired.

"How was your day?" Naomi asked, hours later when I came home at the end of the day.

But she didn't wait for my answer as she turned and headed upstairs. Her question had been merely rhetorical, almost reflexive. We'd both known it. She and I were broken. But I didn't care, not anymore. I had a new focus and another woman who wanted me. I felt better about myself than I had for a long time.

I warmed up some leftovers and went to my computer to check my email and eat my dinner. Naomi was at her usual perch, settled in for the night with her iPad and TV shows. On most any other night, I'd have felt irritated with Naomi's indifference toward me. But I'd decided it was our marriage that had become stale, not me. In an odd sort of way, I even felt relieved I'd found something to fill the void that had been growing within myself.

But deep down, that little voice we all have inside of us told me what I was doing wasn't right. I knew it, even then, since I knew enough to get myself a separate credit card, one Naomi knew nothing about, so I could fly under the radar and explore my newfound freedom on my own terms. Honestly, I was forced into getting the credit card when I tried to pay for a hotel room with cash.

"I'm sorry, sir," the desk clerk had said, "but we'll have to have a credit card for the reservation."

As the English proverb goes, "Necessity is the mother of invention." In this case, it was also the answer to my brief conundrum. That little piece of plastic made it so easy for me to book hotels, flights, car rentals, restaurants, and more. Unbeknownst to my wife, I easily sent flowers, purchased gifts, bought dinners, paid for sex toys, and did anything I wanted without fear of detection. I simply paid the credit card statement online and no paper statements were ever mailed to our home. Alexander D. Banks basically had a whole separate life outside of his lackluster, dull, uninspired one at home. Oh, and what a life he enjoyed!

. . .

The moment I snapped the leather collar around Brooke's neck, her shoulders relaxed, and she seemed more at home than ever before. She was putty in my hands as I gently led her toward the mirror and had her face her reflection as I stood behind her. She was nude, but I was still fully clothed. It was part of retaining my power as I'd learned by this time. At first, she seemed a bit uncomfortable in front of the mirror, but I began to caress her skin and knead her flesh as I stood behind her. We were in no rush. There was time— plenty of time.

"Look at you," I said. "Look at how beautiful you are."

Hesitantly, she stole a glance at the mirror, but I took her chin, lifted it, and repeated, "Look at yourself. Look!"

She was not a hard-body sexpot, not by any stretch of the imagination. In fact, she was very much the non-descript, plain mom. Her body looked like that of a mid-forties woman who had previously birthed a child. Gravity had taken its toll, just like time had. She wasn't perfect, but then, neither was I. Maybe it was because she had kindly filled a void for me that I wanted to return the favor. Who knows? Perhaps it was simply because I knew what a woman needs to feel good about herself, and I wanted to deliver hers so I could then satiate myself.

At first, Brooke tried not to look at her own reflection, maybe afraid to meet her flaws. But I knew what she needed and what I needed to make her feel if I were going to get to my own goal. She needed to feel desirable in my eyes. She needed to feel I saw beyond any surface imperfections or the ravages of time we all experience. I knew because I'd been an imperfect guy, myself. I also knew because I had my own needs and objectives for our time together.

I kneaded her shoulders from behind as I stood against her and breathed in her hair. As she relaxed and sighed, I stroked the outsides of her arms and felt the tiny rise of the smallest hairs on the back of her neck. She moaned in delight. I gave her just a few moments to enjoy the slower pace.

"Do you even know how beautiful you are?" I asked as I nuzzled her neck and she moved against me.

She tried to reach for me, but I moved her hands and forced her to stand facing forward without touching me. I wanted her to focus only on herself and her feelings. The first few innings of our game would be hers. I'd get mine later—and maybe even go back for seconds and hit a grand slam. For now, though, I was in control of her destiny and she enjoyed that reality.

Time passed slowly that afternoon, much slower than it ever had when I'd been busy with customers or working in my office. Gone were the external stresses of vendors, orders, shipments, contractors, employees, and endless daily pressures that usually weighed me down. It was as if I'd left all that behind and left the old Alex behind, too. The man in the hotel room with Brooke was still a bit new to me, but I really liked the guy and how he made me feel. As I cuffed Brooke to the bed, she writhed in anticipation and lifted her hips off the bed to plead for my touch. Just as she'd promised, she had brought along not one, but two, cucumbers for our afternoon of play. I flogged Brooke's backside as she begged for more. In time, her pleasure went from a slow flowing stream to a rapidly raging river, and she cried out when she finally climaxed.

Sex with Brooke was anything but boring and vanilla. It felt like I'd finally been born; I had broken out of my shell and burst into the world, this powerful eruption of a man. With my release also came the liberation of the old Alex, that guy who'd stood on the sidelines, unable for so long to break into inner circles. I let him go, and in his place was Alexander D. Banks, a dominant, omnipotent man, ready to take on the world and finally live in it on his own terms.

It was such a relief finally to be free and know who I was meant to be. I didn't even worry about what might happen if Naomi found out about my other life. I just wanted to live it and savor every second! If Brooke and I didn't have a lot of time, we still met and had wild, unbridled sex in the back of my pickup. There were times when I inwardly laughed and wondered if that was how it was supposed to have been when I was a kid. But *that* Alex had been far too worried about losing his sure bet, that cute girl he'd met on campus with the long gray coat. *That* Alex had been raised to play it safe, to follow the rules, and to take the best opportunity that appeared in the moment. While the *new* Alexander D. Banks was still a bit of an enigma, even to me, there was no doubt he was superior and dominant in his personality. Just that knowledge had made me walk taller, shoulders back, head higher, and maybe with a cockier swagger in my step. Hell, I felt so good about myself that even my black Herman Munster shoes couldn't bring me down! I was living the life of a virile twenty-year-old, ready to grab life by the balls as I bounded from bed with each new sunrise, eager to greet the day and what might unfold. If I could have bottled that powerful energy and indomitable spirit, I'd be a billionaire today, many times over!

For the next year, Brooke and I continued our clandestine meetings, hotel hideaways, dinners, lunches, and as much backseat truck sex as I could fit into my workdays. I thought about getting a "If the truck's a rockin', don't come a knockin'" license plate frame for my truck, but Naomi might ask about my unusual choice—that is, if she even noticed it. Brooke talked often about her son. She'd told me when we'd first met that she never liked to bring men home to meet him until she knew for sure there'd be a long-term relationship. I understood. I'd have done the same with my kids. But meeting Brooke in hotels was fun, and it added another layer of mystique to our arrangement, probably for both of us. She got to leave her life behind, and so did I as we came together.

Fortunately, since I owned a business, I had reason to go on trips for conferences, seminars, and trade shows. Naomi had never really been interested in my business. It wasn't odd to her when I told her I'd be gone for a long weekend or even the better part of a week. If she needed me, she knew I was accessible on my cell phone and that was all she cared about. But sometimes I really did take Brooke along on my business-related trips, in addition to our personal rendezvous. If old colleagues asked about my wife, I simply told them Naomi and I weren't doing well and we'd be divorcing soon. Brooke simply smiled and nodded as she let me do most of the talking. No one really cared. They were caught up in their own agendas.

But apparently, one person had taken notice of me. My brother and business partner came into my office one day, sat down, and stared at me across my desk. I stopped working on my computer and looked at him.

"What? What is it?" I asked.

"You tell me, man. What's been going on with you?"

"What do you mean?"

"Don't give me that. I know you, Alex. You're whizzing around here with the energy of twelve Clydesdales on crack. You're up to something, and it's been going on for months, maybe five or six, I'd say."

Then he stopped talking, raised his eyebrows knowingly, and cocked his head as if waiting for me to spill it. I got up and shut my door. He'd been my brother long enough that I couldn't keep it secret from him any longer. As I sat down behind my desk again, my brother settled back in his chair, confident that he was about to get an earful. Being a guy, I got straight to the point and didn't mince words. If he wanted warm and fuzzy, feel-good sentiments, he could go to the Hallmark Channel. As I spoke, his mouth dropped open and his eyes grew huge. He leaned forward, and again, cocked his head, this time in shock and awe.

"Man, I don't know whether to get up and high-five you or to suggest that you have your head examined!" he laughed. "But yeah, uh, yeah, that sure would explain the extra pep in your step and this newfound bravado thing you've got going on. But you think Naomi knows nothing about what's been going on?"

"Nah, she pays me no attention, trust me. She's in her own little world."

As much as I'd felt I owed it to my brother to tell him the truth about my secret life and what I'd been doing, he also had some strong feelings and opinions of his own. It felt good to finally talk to someone about what I'd been experiencing. My brother wasn't critical of my cheating on Naomi, only curious about my non-stop energy and new lease on life.

"Buddy, you need to make a decision and quick," he said. "You're in a good position. Now's the best time for you to decide what you really want."

I told him I'd give it some thought, but the truth was I needed to get out of my office and go meet Brooke. My mind was laser-focused on the wild, raucous evening ahead. By this time, even my truck headed toward Brooke like a magnet, unable to resist the force that pulled us closer. Each time I left Brooke, I felt like a young college guy who'd just discovered the secret to the Universe. Energetic and rejuvenated, I felt almost superhuman, like I could take on the world. When I took charge and exerted dominance over Brooke, I never felt more alive and yet more serenely at peace. I was no longer that clumsy square peg that could never fit into the round hole, as that old idiomatic expression goes. Alexander had emerged and overshadowed my previous self, and I knew there was no going back.

Whenever Brooke and I met, neither one of us could wait to get on with what we'd both come for that day. At first, I hadn't been sure if I'd gone to the situation to become the new, omnipotent Alexander, or if I had metamorphosed into the newer version of myself. But as time went on, I realized it was the latter; I had been Alexander all along, but I'd never had the opportunity to let him rise to the surface. Finally, I was free to be whom I'd been born to be. I basked in my newfound liberation, just as much as Brooke bathed in her role as my submissive. We'd both found what we'd needed at just the right time in our lives, and our arrangement was about so much more than just sex.

Thanks to first pacing our liaisons, I controlled our time together. We both understood that would be my role, and that I would satisfy Brooke and then do whatever my heart desired to satiate myself. To a guy who'd been sexually stagnant for decades, I felt like I'd been let loose in a candy store, allowed to sample any and all flavors within my reach! I savored my time with Brooke, tasting the sweetness of it and the freedom she allowed me, cloistered away from the realities of our real lives. Later, tired but satisfied like after a grand holiday meal, Brooke and I showered and said our goodbyes.

The peace and clarity I felt when I left her lasted for the rest of the day. Yet hours later, I once again ached for the heady rush of power I'd felt when we'd been together. I couldn't wait to be with her again to drink from the fountain—the only thing that quenched the new Alexander's thirst like nothing else. At times, I laughed at myself, sure I knew what it was like to be a college kid who'd found his willing, nubile sexual playmate. Fortunately, after *Dancing with the Stars*, or Naomi's other nightly shows, had ended, I became more successful in convincing her we should have sex in our bed. We went from having predictable, ten-minute sex every couple of weeks, to having nightly one-and-a-half-hour sex, all because my libido had spiked, compliments of "new Alexander" and his take-charge personality. It amused me that, as a middle-aged guy, I was very likely getting more sex than many college-aged guys. It astounded me that I was able to maintain the energy to satisfy multiple women, but I don't know of too many men who wouldn't be up to attempting the challenge.

By this time, Brooke and I were dating regularly. She'd introduced me to her son. I went over to her house. Her son regarded me as his mom's boyfriend, the guy his mother was dating. Of course, he didn't know I was married, and I preferred to keep it that way. I had a good gig going and wasn't planning to rock the boat. I'd begun to feel better about myself than ever before in my life; I was having more and better sex than ever before, and I'd finally found out who I was meant to be in this world. Life was looking up.

CHAPTER 7

A NEW LIFESTYLE

As Brooke and I continued to experiment with our sexual lifestyle, I wanted to learn more about my role as a dominant and her role as a submissive. One day, she mentioned there was a club we could go to where we could watch others in their sex play, learn, and even participate, ourselves. At first, I felt a bit hesitant. For most of my life, I'd been self-conscious and felt ashamed of my body. But that had been the old Alex. I had morphed into the new Alexander by now, and *he* feared nothing and no one.

"Let's do it!" I agreed.

The night we entered the club was like entering a whole new world. But then, I was also a whole new person. I'd brought along the toys in my toy box, my handcuffs, canes, and floggers, and I was ready to jump in and become part of the club's activities. But first, since I was a newbie, I would have to be vetted and approved by current club members. We met at a secondary location, talked, and they gave me the once-over. I guessed I had passed muster when the club's owner asked if I'd like to go on over to the club and check it out. I liked that they didn't just open their doors to anyone and everyone. A bit of discretion was appreciated.

Brooke was eager for me to cuff her and chain her to the St. Andrew's Cross inside the club and begin our play. She loved that "X" shaped crossing of wood beams that has "D" ring attachments at the top and bottom for chains and clasps to attach to. She just loved to be restrained spread-eagle on the wood, bound by not only the cuffs and chains but also by her sensual need to be controlled. I wanted to tour the dungeon to get the lay of the land. Maybe it was the male in me, but I wanted to find out more about the unusual BDSM club and its members. Brooke and I walked around, mingled with people, made small talk, and occasionally stopped to watch the public demonstrations of flagellations or other techniques being offered. All sorts of contraptions and devices were all around the club, some in use, and others that interested me but I hadn't quite figured out, not just yet anyway. For some reason, I found myself drawn to the chains, always the chains in the scenes. Something about the cold, smooth links and their organized continuity had always fascinated me.

"Have you seen enough yet?" Brooke asked in a hopeful, urgent tone as she and I wandered through the club-goers, most scantily dressed.

"You're eager tonight!" I laughed.

I'd seen how her eyes lit up as we had watched the flogging demonstrations. Her nipples had become erect and stood at attention behind the pink lacey negligee she wore from the moment we'd stopped at the first padded spanking bench. I knew she wished she was the one splayed out face down on that table and taking the delicious lashings. But making her wait was part of my control technique. Besides, the anticipation would make it even better for her.

"Be patient, woman. *I* say when it's time," I reminded her.

I walked to the next scene where a shirtless man stood over a nude woman. She lay on a bench before him with a ball gag in her mouth and tears running from her eyes. He dripped hot, red wax on her bare breasts as she writhed beneath him. The wax ran down the sides of her breasts and dried hard on her skin as she rose up, lost in a mix of heated pain from the candle wax, a pleasure only she understood. Beneath her was a pale blue satin sheet she'd brought along, but very little wax had made it all the way to the sheet. Most had dried on her fair skin.

"Soy candles are best to use," Brooke whispered to me. "They burn cooler and dry quicker."

"Shh! I'll tell you when to speak!"

She knew we would soon begin our own play. Brooke smiled in knowing anticipation as she stopped talking and we both continued to watch the wax play in front of us. When I was ready to leave, I walked off. I knew she would follow without question, eager and right on my heels. I found an available cross that wasn't in use and placed my case on a nearby table behind it. Once Brooke wordlessly removed her negligee, she was nude, except for her thin, silk panties. Eagerly, she went to the cross and stood with her back to me and her arms outstretched and slightly above her head. I affixed her wrists on either side and avoided eye contact with my submissive, focused only on my task at hand. Next, I harnessed Brooke's ankles to the lower "D" ring restraints on each side of the St. Andrew's Cross. Since I knew Brooke was eager and ready, I purposely took my time. When Brooke was properly restrained and spread-eagle, I went to my case to select just the right tool for my work. But first, before I picked it up, I grabbed a ball gag and the red satin blindfold. I went over and put the gag in my sub's willing mouth and placed the blindfold on her face so she'd have no idea what would be coming at her or when it would contact her bare flesh. Again, the control and the anticipation were part of the heightened experience. Her vulnerability was part of what excited her so.

As I looked at her form from behind, I decided one more thing was needed, not for restraint, but for my pleasure. I picked up a length of white, metal-linked chain and additionally chained her ankles. I crossed the chain between her legs and then fastened it together at the ends. The sight of her in chains was a gift I gave to myself.

I then selected a medium leather-handled flogger with leather tails, just to start, and I went to work on my sub. I started out slowly with light flicks of my wrist so that the leather tails contacted Brooke's back and ass cheeks, just enough to let her know I was there, but not nearly enough to satiate her or feed her need. As she squirmed and moaned, I knew she wanted more, so I increased my intensity, but only one time, just enough to give her a taste, nothing more, and then I put away my tool and went and gently massaged the marks on her flesh with my bare hand, just for a moment. Since she couldn't see me, she had no idea I'd picked up my larger, heavier flogger. When I stepped back and then whipped it across her ass, Brooke jumped in delight and squealed her appreciation. Onlookers in the club came closer to watch our display as I increased the lashings' intensity and frequency. Brooke threw her head back and balled her fists tightly as she pressed her stomach against the padded board at her midsection, unable to go anywhere else. Marks began to appear on Brooke's back and upper buttocks, but I was careful not to break her skin. My goal was to keep her on the precipice between pain and pleasure, right on the edge, but not to push her over the edge and do damage. I'd been studying proper techniques, and I must say, I'd gotten pretty good in my new dominant role—as evidenced by the appreciative moaning woman in front of me.

After I'd given Brooke a good lashing, I put down my final tool. Then I gently stroked the marks on her flesh and kissed the pink and red lines that told the story of the last half hour of her life. Her body tingled in a different anticipation now, a gentle peace, that cooled and calmed her, as tiny goosebumps popped up all over her skin and the tiniest hairs on her flesh stood at attention. I kissed her back and then her thighs, and I tasted the salt of her sweat as she shuddered under my touch. I knew she wanted me to remove the blindfold and take the gag from her mouth. But I enjoyed taking down, just as much as I'd enjoyed taking up, the rollercoaster of passion she'd ridden. Her experience was in my hands; what happened next was entirely up to me, and we both knew it. I thrived under that knowledge in the dimly lit room as music played around us. All the onlookers had moved on, so Brooke and I were alone now. She was lost in the downward spiral as she freefell toward the end of her session.

"Here, I'll take those now," I finally said as I removed the blindfold and took the gag from her mouth.

When I removed the restraints at her ankles, and then her wrists, Brooke almost fell into me. She was so weak and spent. She looked up into my eyes, entirely at peace and fully relaxed. I handed her the nearby glass of water, and I let her lean on me as she took a sip and steadied herself. As I held her up with one arm, I finished putting away my tools and shut my case with the other. We then silently went upstairs to a place we'd seen when we had toured the club earlier. I knew I had to have her, then and there, and from what I'd seen before, it looked like that was the place couples went to have sex. Only a few people were in the loft area, and they seemed to be engrossed in one another. Minutes later, Brooke and I began to earn our moniker of "The Loud Couple" in that club, as I got the second payoff of what I'd come for on that night. For a guy who'd once been ashamed of his body, it was amazing, even to me, that I was having sex in a semi-public venue and feeling nothing but mighty and powerful, like I could take over the world. What a memorable night that turned out to be as I fully transitioned to the role of dominant exhibitionist and zestfully owned my newfound persona.

Being with Brooke turned into my favorite pastime. She was such a willing partner, and her sense of adventure and eagerness to please me made her seem more attractive than she really was. It was the ideal of that person that I was drawn to, I believe.

"Where are we going today?" Brooke asked when we got in my truck.

"Where do you want to go?"

"A friend told me about this secluded beach with a quiet cove where she goes to watch whales as they migrate. I thought of you and how you'd said you'd like to just escape from reality, even for a little while. Let's go check it out. I'll call the office and tell them I won't be in today."

I didn't hesitate. The thought of a quiet, secluded beach sounded perfect to me after the week I'd had. I didn't want to go back to the office.

"I think I just took the day off," I laughed as I headed my truck toward the coast.

We'd already had sex that morning as soon as I'd gotten to her house. Brooke knew I'd had a hell of a week. Dozens of things had gone wrong at the office, Naomi was pissed off about several things, and the pressures had begun to mount on me. So Brooke's suggestion that we play hooky had been a welcome one.

"I know how busy you are," she said as she held my hand. "I love every stolen moment and each delicious hour we have together."

It felt good to be needed, to be wanted. Alone in the truck with Brooke, I felt important to her, like I mattered. Her attention focused only on me as if she needed and wanted just me. When I stopped at a grocery store, we walked hand in hand through the aisles and selected items for our picnic basket. Breads, cheeses, smoked meats, fresh fruits, chocolates, and two bottles of wine quickly filled our cart. Back in the truck, we listened to music as we rode along.

"There's a rainforest along our route," Brooke said as she looked at her cell phone. "It says there's a serene mountain lake and we can take a short walk through the woods."

"Sure. Why not?"

"Looks like it's about thirty miles before the beach exit."

A little while later, I saw the sign for the rainforest. I slowed, took the exit, and drove into the designated entrance, but the place was deserted. As we drove along the dirt road, dust and gravel trailed behind my truck until I came to a parking area and stopped. We got out and hiked a short distance toward the mountain lake, using the signs as our guides. Tall pine trees towered above us and pine scent filled the air with a peaceful freshness that relaxed me to the bone.

"What a view," Brooke said as we looked out over the glistening lake.

"Majestic."

I pulled her to me and hugged her as we took in the scenery and breathed in nature's scents. The stress evaporated from me and left through my pores as the gentle breeze carried it away. I closed my eyes and let the warm sun's rays bathe my face as I inhaled my newfound relaxation.

"Ready to go?" I asked Brooke.

We went back to my truck and got on the road again, but we didn't get very far. The urgent bulge in my pants refused to be ignored. As Brooke ran her hand down my thigh, I looked for a side road or a clearing within the trees, anyplace where I might pull off the road. Soon, I came upon an overgrown forest workers' backroad that had been long forgotten. But it was no match for my big truck; I easily drove through the brush and into the forest as the bushes closed again behind my truck so it was entirely out of sight from the road. Without a word, Brooke and I got out and went to the bed of the truck. I put down the tailgate and then spread a blanket over it. Brooke had already unbuttoned and unzipped her shorts, and I helped her out of them. Then I lifted her up onto the tailgate. She lay back, ready to receive me, already full and hard.

At first, Brooke looked into my eyes as I entered her slowly. But as my rhythm increased, her back arched to meet me, and she held on to me as her stare was lost in the birch leaf canopy above us. The harder I pumped into her warm wetness, the louder she moaned in delight. We were each lost in our own pleasure as we climbed higher and higher. As I got closer and thrusted faster and harder, she opened her eyes to witness my ecstasy as I went over the edge.

Still hard, I continued thrusting, but slower and more teasing now, just to remind her who was in control. Brooke's throaty moans pleaded for more, and she lifted her hips to meet my thrusts, but I ignored her urgent pleas and made her wait. Her pulsating wetness clamped down on my cock and silently begged for release.

"Would you like for me to make your day?" I asked, smiling.

She nodded, and I reached for the nearby bag as I continued to thrust into her. Brooke watched as I took out the handcuffs, a collar, a leash, and leather straps and quickly bound her so she'd be under my total control. As I slowly pumped into her swollen flesh,

I treated her quivering clit to the vibrator I'd brought along for her. In no time, echoes of her pleasured screams filled the forest and birds flew from their roosts in the treetops. But I wasn't done with her, not yet. Before she caught her breath, I took her to the edge again, not once, but twice. After three orgasms, Brooke lay spent and unable to move.

"Let me help you get dressed." I laughed as I lifted her and helped her to stand. "Your legs are shaking."

We continued our drive to the coast, both relaxed and exhausted, all at once. Not a single stress filled my mind. Not the first worry bothered me. I felt peaceful and relaxed as we got closer to the cove Brooke's friend had recommended. Not a care in the world was on my mind, only the day that lay ahead with the willing, agreeable woman beside me. Her only goal was to take care of my every need. I wasn't thinking beyond that immediate space and time, that comfort and easy pace that I savored within the confines of my truck where I blocked out all the stresses and tensions of the real world.

After a while, the sea came into view. I rolled down my truck's windows and opened the sunroof to invite in the salty air, and I turned off the radio. Instantly, the cab was filled with seagulls' chatter and lazy water sounds as the gentle surf lapped the shore. Not a car was in sight and not a single person on the shoreline for as far as we could see. I parked near a bluff, shut off the engine, and shut my eyes to allow the sounds and scents to bathe me, even drown me. Brooke reached over and gently rubbed my left thigh and kissed my neck.

"Oh, no, little wench," I said, laughing. "First, we eat. I'm starved."

We got our picnic foods, a heavy blanket, my camera equipment, and our chairs from the bed of my truck and then made our way across the sand. The gentle wind blew seagrasses as we cut through a small footpath toward the shoreline. Seagulls above us swooped lower for a closer look, hopeful we might have something for their lunch, too. Little sandpipers busied themselves on the hard-packed sand, looking for insects or baby crabs that burrowed deeper to escape their fates. I said nothing, but I was reminded of how hard I'd worked to escape my own fate, the boring monotony of my bland, vanilla life that had threatened to consume me.

Shaking off the notion so as not to ruin my day, I said, "Hey, let's walk up the beach and around the bend." Brooke didn't answer. She silently followed me as we turned toward the beautiful rocky cove up the beach to see what was just out of sight to us. With my drone cases slung over my shoulders, along with camera equipment, and carrying our picnic basket and chairs, I was loaded down, but I wanted to find a spot that would be all ours for the day. Brooke carried a tote bag and the blue plaid blanket, along with two light windbreakers we'd brought along.

"Hey, how's it going?" I nodded to the lone fisherman with his long surf rod and tackle box as he approached us.

"Great! Saw a whale an hour ago. Keep an eye out." He smiled.

"We will; thanks. Good luck with the perch today."

"Thanks!"

Brooke linked her arm through mine and we continued on our way. I was sure the man thought she was my wife and that Brooke enjoyed his presumption, but I didn't care. We walked wordlessly for a few more minutes until we came to a private cove bordered on one side by rocks and the other by the sea. It felt like we were at the edge of the world and at a place where all my problems no longer mattered and couldn't touch or even find me. Not a soul knew my whereabouts. My time was my own. The day was in front of me to do with as I chose—just as I should have looked at *life*, decades earlier. But all I had was the day, so I had to make the most of it and savor every moment.

Brooke set up our campsite for the day and arranged our hide-away from reality. I pulled out my larger drone and set it up to do aerial shots of the impressive scenery so I could later revisit the majestic coastline and, hopefully, recall how peaceful I'd felt that day. Brooke sipped her Pinot Noir and watched as I went over my drone's preflight checklist.

"How come you don't use that more often? And why don't you do your photography more? I know how much you love it, and you're a really good photographer, Alex."

"No time, I guess. There's always something else to do."

"But it makes you so happy. Right now, even. You look relaxed, even ten years younger, out here and doing what you love."

"Gotta get ahead, right? Work always calls. My lifestyle won't pay for itself." I laughed.

Her comments irked me in a way, like she judged me or how I'd chosen to spend my time. She clearly coveted the life I lived, my home, the trips, the money, everything. Yet Brooke couldn't seem to connect the dots and understand that one has to put in the time and effort to earn his way into such a position. It had been a series of choices and sacrifices. I tried to shake off the twinge of irritability I felt and not let it creep into my day. I only wanted to play hooky from life, just for a few glorious hours. As I flew my drone and concentrated on the screen, Brooke alternately watched me and watched the drone as it flew across the water and the rocky coastline. "I love to watch you when you're doing what you really love and you're nurturing your creativity. I wish you'd do it more often," she said. I didn't answer, but it wasn't lost on me that Naomi didn't even seem to remember I was a photographer, much less care whether I pursued something I enjoyed. I tried to shake off the conflicting conversations in my head and simply concentrate on the screen in my hands.

A little while later, Brooke and I ate the lunch she'd prepared for us and shared the rest of the bottle of Pinot Noir she'd opened, and then I opened a bottle of Merlot. The sun had moved in the sky and it felt warmer, maybe even a bit hot, as we sat in our beach chairs. As I ate a cheese chunk, I saw Brooke watching me. I knew she'd have preferred if I savored it and allowed the cheese to melt lazily on my palate. But I chewed it, perhaps to spite her, I'll admit, and then I ate another one and took a man-sized swig of wine.

"It's getting hot. Let's move back closer to the rocks," I said as I got up to move my chair and the picnic basket.

Brooke did the same, and then we sat down again. I leaned back, reclined my chair a bit, and shut my eyes with Brooke beside me in her chair. Full of lunch and feeling the wine, we listened to the seagulls and the sound of water gently touching the shore and receding, over and over again. The rhythm was tranquil and hypnotizing. Brooke took my hand and held it for a few minutes.

"Ready for your dessert now?" she asked just as I was about to nod off.

Before I could answer, she'd knelt in front of me and begun unzipping my pants. I was fully erect, even before my pants were off. *Those* were the only oral sounds I wanted to hear from Brooke as I held her head in my hands and closed my eyes to listen to the birds and sea. Minutes later, as if someone had turned up its intensity, the surf increased and the waves crashed louder and harder against the shore as I, too, erupted in pleasure.

"Okay, I definitely need that nap now."

"I'll let you sleep now," she said, laughing.

While I lay spent and dozing, Brooke walked along the shoreline on the smooth rocks at the water's edge. Like myself, all those rocks had been slowly eroded over time, changed by the elements, altered by the forces around them. Those rocks under Brooke's feet would also never be the same; their natural jagged edges had been replaced by softened corners, smoothed sides, and slick facades. No one would ever know the original rocks or what they'd once been when they'd first come into being. I was the same—altered, changed, and adapted to fit into the world as others had seen fit, often at the cost of my own happiness.

"Hey, lover, look what I found for you." Brooke's voice woke me. She held a smooth, white quartz stone in her palm and smiled down at me, almost like a proud child who'd just discovered a grand treasure. The sun was behind her, so I squinted to make out her face, but I clearly saw the white stone and took the offering as I sat up in my beach chair and lazily stretched.

"I thought it'd look great on your desk as a paperweight," she added. "It'll be your reminder of our perfect day at the coast, and when the stress of your workday is on you, then you can look at this stone and remember our time together. Only you and I will know what it is, our little secret." She knelt down and kissed me, long and deep, and then added, "And you can remember how I stole that last kiss at the end of our special day."

It was getting late; she was right, but I hated to leave our private nook, the clandestine hideaway from life's realities and stresses. We reluctantly packed up our campsite and slowly walked up the beach under the late afternoon sun. When my truck came into sight, my shoulders tensed. Life awaited. But I held it off for as long as I could, taking the scenic route and driving us along the coastline and through the forest. We stopped in a quaint beachside town to get Brooke an espresso and a water for me, and then we continued on our way.

I wanted to take some sunset photos at another coastal spot on our route. When I pulled into a sand dune area near the beach, the sun was still above the water. We had a little time to kill, and I knew just how to do it. "Come on," I told Brooke as I got out. I went to the back of my truck for the blanket and to retrieve the tube of lubricant from her tote bag.

Brooke veritably skipped toward the beach, eager to let me take her in the dunes. I laughed at her willingness to please me and allow me to do whatever I liked. For a guy who'd had to conform and who had been forced to fall in line with others' expectations, this was a welcome gift. Brooke's eagerness and willingness were aphrodisiacs enough for me. No foreplay was needed. I was hard and ready, even before she'd stripped off her clothes and knelt in the submissive position to receive me. It was her favorite position anyway, and she was always willing to go straight to it without hesitation. The grasses were tall, and I could see from my vantage point if anyone approached from any direction. But I hurried to apply the lube and enter her warm, waiting flesh to claim her as my willing sex submissive. Instantly, I was lost in the perfect liberation and rolling in the waves of pleasure that washed over both of us.

"Still some time before sunset," I said a little while later. "Let's get some chowder at that place with the outdoor deck up the road that we passed, the one I went to as a kid."

Brooke thought I wanted to share a special place with her from my youth, but I just wanted to get some of their clam chowder while I was in the area. It was amazing to me how the woman could romanticize every little thing. We sat side by side, each lost in our own thoughts, but I now know they were probably two different dialogues that played in our heads: I was eating chowder, but she was planning our future. After we ate, I stopped at a little shop for some saltwater taffy, also just like I'd done as kid. For me, I had simply felt like some taffy. For Brooke, it was a bonding moment in which I had gone out of my way to share my favorite childhood candy with her.

By the time we got back to the dunes, the sun had just begun to lick the ocean's surface, barely tasting its salty goodness and lazily easing into its watery haven for the night. I hurried to grab my largest camera and the longest lens I'd brought along, just for the special money shot. I'd taken lots of sunset photos, but this one would memorialize a special day for me. I wanted to get it right. "Come on!" I grabbed Brooke's hand and we ran toward the sea. I was reminded that the moment was one I should have experienced so many years earlier, long before life and obligations had ever crept into my world.

CHAPTER 8

ESCAPING LIFE

No one ever knew about the day I'd played hooky. After that day at the coast, Brooke and I regularly got together for our afternoon trysts and evening rendezvous. Most times, Naomi thought I was at the office or I told her I'd be over at a friend's house for a few hours. But when Brooke and I wanted to spend a few days together, I simply mentioned in passing that I had an upcoming business trip.

"Where's the convention?" Naomi asked one night as she lay on my bed, knees comfortably bent with her iPad resting on her lap. She didn't even lift her head from staring at her iPad as she questioned me. Not a look or a glance came my way.

"It's the Wood Flooring Expo. They're holding it in Fort Worth."

That was it, end of conversation. My wife was satisfied. She knew I would be only as far away as my cell phone, and that appeased her. The truth was there was indeed a hardwood flooring expo, but Brooke and I would be handling some hard wood of a different species, too. I already knew all about *this* particular wood, where it grew, how long it lasted, its durability, how long it needed to acclimate, and how well it held up to excessive traffic, and I knew the importance of laying it right the first time.

When I packed for my trip, I tossed in several outfits, including one dinner jacket. It was the first time I packed for a trip without packing in our old master bedroom of our home. I had moved into another bedroom, the one my parents had once shared. Oddly, I'd begun to notice Naomi had started to realize she and I had a major disconnect. She didn't realize just how bad things were, not yet anyway, but she had an inkling, if a fleeting one.

Brooke liked fancy restaurants, fine wines, exotic cheeses, and menu items neither of us could pronounce, but that sounded expensive. I enjoyed wines, too, but with Brooke it was different. She almost felt it her duty to reach a bit higher than where she might ordinarily feel socially comfortable in all situations. She liked to select a pricier wine, just to appear as astute as the sommelier, even if she hadn't a clue whether the wine might pair with her chosen cuisine. I'd always been the type of guy who either liked a wine, or I didn't, plain and simple. I didn't need to pontificate about all the notes of heightened boysenberry and the hint of Moroccan amber that had been deftly infused and aerated into the damned bottle. I didn't care if I could separate the nuanced herb from the earthly coffee bean notes in the Bordeaux. Just pour me the damned wine, and I'll let you know if it's a go, or not.

Yet to Brooke, it was a dance, a seductive, choreographed production, just to get a damned glass of wine. I had a wife at home, watching *Dancing with the Stars*, and I had another woman with me who enjoyed doing her mating dance ritual every time we sat down to order a drink. What was it with these women? But it wasn't just Brooke's wine affinity we indulged. She was like that about cheese, too. Now, I like a tasty cheese. But just put some cheese cubes on a plate and I'll pick them up and go to town. I don't need to take time to consider which cheese will pair best with my wine. I don't want to slowly tongue the cheese in my mouth, allowing it to lazily melt and mingle on my palate so all the flavors open up, one layer at a time. It seemed like overkill to me to intellectualize cheese tasting and to appreciate its look, color, texture, silkiness, and whether it had a fine, smooth aftertaste. The damned cheese was as complicated as the wines, it seemed. I tried to participate, to let her enjoy the decadent cheese appetizers she'd ordered before dinner, but it seemed ridiculous to me, a big, strapping, full-grown man, to do the same.

"Alexander, let it lay on your tongue," said Brooke, smiling. "Just wait. Can you taste the fennel first, and then the chive, just a touch, ever so faintly?"

I started chewing and washed the cheese down with a big gulp of Merlot. She was not pleased.

"Seriously? I wanted you to get the full effect! Each piece is handmade so you'll unveil every layer, one at a time, and the wine enhances the flavor and the finish of both the cheese and wine as they play together."

"It's fucking *cheese*!" I laughed as I outstretched my palms.

We were sitting in the bar of a nice Texas steakhouse. It was one of those places where it's not unusual to see sports figures or celebrities, but where everyone is very discreet because all the diners are uber-wealthy and not impressed by money nor status. Off to one side of the bar was a private, glass-enclosed room. It was stocked with specially labeled private reserve wines for the restaurant's most important clientele, just to make their premier guests feel welcome. I knew Brooke would enjoy the place. I'd been there before, and she'd always appreciated when I had shown her a different world than the one she had known before we'd met. She was dressed in a cocktail dress and heels, and I wore a dinner jacket, as did most other men in the restaurant. With her nails done and her lipstick shining, Brooke fit the part of the other women in the restaurant. I knew it was the life she'd always desired, the world she'd always felt should be her own. But the truth was Brooke was working on herself and trying hard to learn to be the person she thought she wanted to be in this world.

Brooke hadn't had an easy life. She didn't come from wealth, but she'd wanted so badly to belong to what she'd always viewed as "high society." It seemed to me she felt if she could ascend to that point, she could leave her truths and the ugliness of her earlier years so far behind that the world would forget from where she'd come. She tried so hard and worked so diligently to be someone other than the woman she was at the time. Brooke was an intelligent woman. It didn't surprise me. I'd always been attracted to smart women. But she thought she was always the smartest person in the room, and that included when we were together. She was a trained therapist, a practitioner who heard the troubles, stresses, and shortcomings of others. Basically, she helped people develop cognitive and emotional skills to help them find coping mechanisms to deal with their crap. In doing that, Brooke had also developed a grandiose opinion of herself, an omniscient attitude, and an inflated ego. Even the way she held her wine glass seemed smug as she surveyed the fancy bar, casting judgments on those around us. I knew what she was doing. I'd seen it before. Brooke usually put others down as a way to elevate herself. I signaled the bartender that I'd like another drink, and he nodded that he'd be right over.

"Should we get another bottle of Merlot?" I asked Brooke.

"I think I'd like to switch it up." She winked.

I knew what that meant. She was about to put the bartender to the test, her test, probably the biggest test of the poor guy's bartending career. I almost wanted to give him a heads-up as to what was coming, but there was no time.

"Yes, sir!" he said, smiling. "May I get you another bottle of the 2001 Le Macchiole Messorio? How did you and the lady enjoy the first bottle?"

Before I could answer, Brooke piped up. "It was fabulous! Exceptionally polished. It tastes like the rolling hills of Tuscany."

She was a bit tipsy, but her overt, pushy demeanor irritated me. And she'd never been to Tuscany, so I had no idea what in the hell she was talking about with that last statement. Did she think the expensive Merlot tasted like soil, or perhaps manure? I hadn't a clue—and neither did she. Even the bartender seemed caught off-guard, but he remained stoically polite, his professional smile still plastered on his face as Brooke continued her attempt to impress.

"But I think I'd like to switch to a cocktail," she added, just as I'd predicted. "Do you know how to make a cocktail called The Commonwealth?"

She paused and fluttered her eyelashes while the bartender seemed to panic a bit, silently checking his memory bank. She was testing him. We both knew it—no, we *all* knew it. That was what embarrassed me about her pompous show whenever she performed it. She enjoyed putting servers, bartenders, hotel staffers, and other service personnel on the spot, every chance she got. It was as if she thought it elevated her in some way, yet it had always disgusted me. Brooke had not come from a billion-dollar bloodline family. She was not related to the Rockefellers, the Vanderbilts, the Mellons, nor any notable family for that matter. She did not grow up in Palm Beach or attend boarding school, and she'd never summered in the Hamptons.

No, Brooke was a simple woman, a smart woman, but a simple woman who'd come from a working-class family. It seemed she was the only one who had a hard time accepting where she'd come from. No one else cared. Brooke used to enjoy just ordering a Boulevardier, but when she found out about The Commonwealth and how difficult a cocktail it is to make, it became her choice in many situations, especially since it carried with it a hefty price tag, so she sometimes switched it up a bit.

"Oh! Yes!" the bartender finally remembered, obviously relieved. "The Commonwealth! I've only made a couple of those in my whole sixteen-year career. I can definitely make you that cocktail, but the honey won't be from New Zealand and the saffron won't be from Pakistan, I'm afraid. Is that okay? And obviously, the prickly pear won't be from Namibia."

"Do you have the Tanzanian cloves then?" Brooke asked.

"Well, to be honest, that'd be a no, too. But I've got cloves and they're of the highest quality. How about I mix you one and see what you think?"

Brooke feigned disappointment as if her discernible palate might be able to tell the difference between Tanzanian cloves and ones purchased from the Piggly Wiggly down the street, but she nodded that the bartender should scurry off on his errand to concoct the exotic pink cocktail.

"Give me a few minutes," he said. "The Commonwealth has seventy-one ingredients. It'll take me a moment to whip one up, ma'am."

"Go ahead and make it two, buddy," I told him as I motioned with my hand also.

I liked the unique drink with its varied ingredients that melded together. The seventy-one ingredients included things like lemon grass, sweet basil, tamarind, lavender, coconut, coffee beans, devil's claw, rosehip, kava, and more. The flavors were amazing even before the aged whiskey and Grand Marnier ever blended with them. First created by a Glasgow mixologist, the cocktail is properly mixed using specific ingredients from all around the globe. Therefore, it's an expensive delicacy and regarded by many bartenders as the most complicated cocktail on the planet.

"Right away, sir!" The bartender smiled with a tilt of his head.

He and I both knew he was about to start sweating his task at hand as he went to round up most of the necessary ingredients from the restaurant's chef—and the clock was ticking. He and I both also knew that, based on the cost of those two pink drinks, he had a fat tip riding on his mixologist skills. I downed the rest of my Merlot and then sipped from my water glass.

"Wow!" Brooke laughed, with a twinkle in her eye. "Such a girlie drink!"

"What?"

"You just ordered a delicate pink drink that's about to come out in a dainty round champagne glass. Is this my big, bad Dom?"

As I looked dumbfounded at her, I noticed two other gentlemen at the end of the bar listening to our conversation. My attention and sheer embarrassment turned right back in her direction.

She leaned back and looked sideways at me, sizing me up as if she didn't recognize the guy who'd just ordered what she considered a frilly, girlie drink. Suddenly, I felt hot and uncomfortable, like there wasn't enough air in the room.

"That's my big, strong man!" she said, winking. "Aww, look. He's got a softer side."

"Excuse me. You may stop that. Right now."

I glared at her so she knew I meant business. Then I signaled the bartender, who'd just rounded the bar from the backside, carrying a basketful of what I knew had to be some of the ingredients for our drinks.

"Check, please!" I told him.

He came right over, panicked that I might be upset with him.

"I'm sorry, sir. I just had to go to the chef for a couple of the—"

"No, it's fine. Change of plans. I need to be somewhere," I said as I looked at the check and then left him more than enough cash to cover it, plus a nice tip for his troubles.

Brooke said nothing as I grabbed her wrist and wordlessly led her from the bar. She knew I was fuming, clear she'd crossed that imaginary line all subs know exists. Without releasing my grip on her, I guided her toward the elevator, pushed the button to call the car, and silently waited. A few other people were nearby. Brooke knew to say nothing. My anger radiated from me, so much so that I wondered if I glowed red-hot and if others saw it, too. When the elevator doors opened, only Brooke and I walked inside.

"Honey, what's wrong?" she asked when the doors had shut and we were alone.

"You do not *ever* criticize me like that, not *ever*, and especially not in public!" I said through my gritted teeth as I looked down on her.

My body shook and blood rushed to my head. I'd never been so angry in all my life. How dare she belittle me and judge me? How dare she try to call me dainty and frilly because of my choice of drink? I felt betrayed and alone. Suddenly, the woman, the one person I'd thought to be my soulmate, had made a joke of me, cut me down, and humiliated my manhood. Memories and feelings from the past flooded back all at once and threatened to drown me in that enclosed elevator. The tidal wave was coming fast and furious, just as the doors finally parted and let us exit the small confined space. I had to get away from Brooke so I could breathe again. I let go of her wrist and walked away from her in long, fast strides. Soon, I no longer heard the sounds of her high heels on the sidewalk behind me. I just needed to walk and clear my head, to shake off the rage that had boiled to the surface, and I didn't want to lash out and hurt her, even though she'd angered and hurt me.

It had taken me years to feel like I was on top and in control—like I knew who I was in the world. Brooke's betrayal had hit me hard and cut deep. Remembrances of past times and old hurts bubbled to the surface like a long dormant volcano that had finally erupted. Flashbacks of decades earlier, times when I had felt overlooked, forgotten, left out, and less than, had been triggered. It didn't take a fancy degree or a long list of letters behind a doctor's name to figure it out: I still had a lot of crap I hadn't dealt with from my childhood.

But that realization still didn't excuse Brooke's behavior, not in my mind anyway. I had felt she and I had built a relationship on trust, a mutual trust that went both ways. Even behind closed doors when she and I participated in our sex play, we had a degree of trust and a bond I'd felt was special. We had agreed on a "safe word" she would use if she ever felt uncomfortable during our BDSM practices, and one of the first rules in such relationships is that the safe word is always respected and obliged by the dominant in the relationship. The word might mean to stop altogether, or it might mean to reduce the intensity of the act. But when it is uttered by the submissive, it means the dominant must respect it and defer to his sub for instruction on how to proceed. It's the only way the submissive agrees to such a relationship and rightly so. As my and Brooke's relationship had progressed, just as our sex play had progressed, I had entrusted my heart to her. When she'd betrayed me at the bar, I had felt just as hurt as if she'd stomped on my heart with her stilettos—one thing we'd never done in our sex play because it never interested either one of us, frankly. The deep anger and resentment I felt after her betrayal made me begin to rethink whether I should even be with Brooke. How could a woman love me if she'd laugh at me and publicly humiliate me?

Yet I was still a guy and, let's be honest, I had physical needs. Brooke wanted to talk things out, like women do, and I wanted to rip her panties off and punish her like she deserved to be punished. She needed to be reminded who the man was in our relationship. In no time, she and I were back to our old routine of me arriving at her house, stripping her bare-ass naked, bending her over the kitchen table, and taking what I wanted. I was a dominant who needed to have his needs met, and my truck steered toward her as if she were in heat. She knew she'd screwed up. She was willing to oblige me any time, any place, if it meant she wouldn't lose me. Of course, Brooke still thought she was the smartest one in our duo. But seriously, who was smarter? I was getting exactly what I wanted and when I wanted it, no questions asked. Yet she thought she was playing me since she was a therapist, the one who dealt with people and got into their heads.

"You know," she said one night, "my friends keep asking how come I've never been to your house."

"Now you know the answer to that. I don't think Naomi would be thrilled if I brought you by the house. Do you?"

"I've been by your house. It's very nice."

"You've been to my house?"

"I just drove past it. It's very nice. What a view right there on the lake. I'd love to see the inside, though."

She continued to ask to go to my house; over and over, she brought it up. So, one day when Naomi was away, I thought it would be a good time to get it out of the way, just so Brooke would stop harassing me about it.

"Where are we going?" she asked as we rode along in my truck one afternoon.

"To show you my home."

Her eyes lit up like a kid on Christmas morning about to unwrap her most significant gift. Brooke sat up straighter, eager to finally get a look inside my family home that she'd long coveted from the curb. To me, it was just a house, simply brick and mortar that held within its walls decades of memories and plenty of pains I'd prefer to forget. Yet to strangers, the pristine house appeared tidy and orderly, a comfortable family home, most likely a warm and inviting gathering space that welcomed generations to come and stay awhile. To those who knew no better, the sturdy walls appeared to offer shelter and protection. When I'd been a boy, however, I felt exposed to the world, long before I was prepared. Sure, I had good times in the house, like when Naomi and I had spent special times with our son and daughter, and lots of gigantic parties we'd had at the house, and all the times I'd proudly brought home or had delivered the endless stream of electronics, watercrafts, or other lavish toys I'd convinced myself I needed and deserved—tangible proof to myself that I'd worked hard and earned my own success in life. I had talked with my psychologist about all the old memories that still haunted me. We talked about losing Krissy so many years earlier and about how my older siblings had always regarded me as an unwanted inconvenient half-brother whose mother had one day shown up and changed life as they'd known it. All the stories I'd shared had seemed to revolve around our family home or within its walls. One day, I'd wondered aloud if maybe I had wanted to raise my own kids in my childhood home so I could replace some of the negatives with positives and swap out some of the bad vibes for good ones.

"Hey! Did you hear me? Earth to Alex!"

Brooke's voice finally roused me from my memories as I drove along the highway. I had been deep in thought and hadn't heard what she'd said, none of it.

"Oh, sorry. What was that?"

"I asked why you decided to take me and show me your house after I've been asking for so long. Why now?" she repeated.

"Why not?" I shrugged. "And Naomi's away. It's a good time, right?"

Ten minutes later, I turned my truck into our country club neighborhood on the lakefront. Mature trees rose up around sprawling homes that sat amid manicured shrubs and freshly trimmed lawns. The community was affluent, but it was still family-oriented. Some of the homeowners had been in their homes for several generations, like me. Others were successful entrepreneurs, brokers, bankers, a couple of bigwigs from Amazon and a handful of Microsoft executives.

"I just love this whole area," Brooke said as we drove along the country club's main entrance and then past the impressive clubhouse. "You must love living here."

"I've been here for so long I don't really think about it, I guess, but yeah, it's nice. It was a great place to grow up, on the lake and all."

"Yeah, the lake is huge! I drove all through here and saw all the big boats on the water and docked behind the houses. It must've been like growing up in paradise."

"Ha! Paradise." I smirked. "Not quite."

"Yeah, I get it. You told me about some of that crap. But you could have done a lot worse. Take it from me."

I knew what she meant. I'd thought about it before, many times. I wasn't ungrateful, and I'd always been aware that I had been afforded so many opportunities thanks to my parents, and especially to Dad. But he could be a son-of-a-bitch, too, when he wanted.

"Look at these people," Brooke said. "The women are like Stepford Wives in here."

"What?"

"Those women in the golf cart we just passed," she said, laughing, "they were perfectly coiffed, wearing matching designer golf outfits, and those earrings on the driver had to be three-carats, easy—and all to *play golf*!"

"We're going eighteen-miles-per-hour, woman! You seriously just made all those observations as we passed those two women?"

"I don't miss much."

When we got nearer the houses on the water, Brooke took off her seatbelt and leaned forward as if she didn't want to miss anything. Naomi had our kids with her, so I knew the house would be completely empty. I made a left turn and then drove along the winding road until I came to my home. When I stopped in the driveway, Brooke looked surprised.

"Not parking in the garage?"

"Not possible! The garage is packed full of shit—my shit, our shit, my parents' shit, just endless *shit*!"

No one would know it from the outside, and the homeowners' association would certainly not be pleased if I'd dared open the garage door and leave it open for an entire weekend. My garage stood in stark contrast to the pristine country club community outside of it.

"It's kind of like you," Brooke said. "Neat and tidy on the outside but packed full of chaotic shit hidden deep within the walls."

"Don't try to psychoanalyze me; you know I hate that."

It was her way of trying to be smarter and in control of a situation. She'd tried it several times before, and I had despised it each time. Brooke thought she had everyone figured out, even me.

"Let's see where 'Alexander the Great' lives!" she said as she walked ahead of me toward my front door.

I unlocked the door and then let her walk inside, ahead of me, as I watched her reaction. I knew her well enough that I felt sure of how she'd respond. Just as she always responded predictably to my practiced canings and whippings, Brooke did just as I had imagined, right down to her mannerisms and the inflection in her voice.

"My God! That view!" she exclaimed as her shoulders relaxed and she gazed longingly at Mount Rainier right across the lake in its full majesty.

"Everyone's always drawn to it. It can't be beat; that's for sure."

I followed her as she walked toward the sliding glass doors and then out onto the back deck that overlooked the water. Decades earlier, I had proposed to Naomi at those same doors. But so much had changed—including me. I wasn't the same man I had been back then. My marriage to Naomi wasn't the same. My wife wasn't the same. Somehow, when I walked out onto my back deck and followed Brooke, it felt like I stepped toward my future with one foot, yet my other foot was still firmly planted on the other side of the doorway, still in my marriage. Again, the house, my home that held so many memories and emotions, was the root of my angst, the holder of my secrets.

"I'll bet you spend a lot of time out here with your kids," Brooke said when I walked up behind her.

"Not as much as I'd like, not even close. It's my damned diabetes and my foot ulcers that are the problem. I can't get my feet wet, like

I told you. It's hard for me to have all these water toys and the boat out here, but I can't use them with the kids like my dad did with me."

"Do you and Naomi sit out here, with wine?"

"Not in a long, long time, no. In fact, I can't even remember the last time we sat out here together at all."

"Well, if I were your wife, I'd have dinner cooking on the stove and a drink in your hand the minute you came through the door," Brooke said as she wrapped her arms round my neck and kissed me, "and I'd sit out here with you, and we'd watch the sun set every night hand in hand."

I knew what she was doing. I'd known it from the moment I'd swung open the front door for her and allowed her to step into my innermost sanctuary, my family home. In Brooke's mind, she already saw herself as "the lady of the manor." Gone from her contrived reality were all traces of Naomi. Brooke coveted the impressive home, the country club lifestyle, and the perceived high society status she presumed went with those things. All she had to do was simply pluck Naomi from the picture and position herself as my new wife, as if she and my current spouse were interchangeable pawns on a chessboard. The notion reminded me of what it must have been like decades earlier when Dad came home and announced that my siblings should remove their mom's photos from the house because their new mom would be moving in soon.

"Don't you think, Alex?" Brooke said.

"Think? Think what?"

"Did you hear anything I just said?"

"Sorry; I was thinking about something. What did you say?"

"Never mind. Show me the rest of the house." She shrugged.

There was no denying I'd begun to question whether Brooke was right for me. Sure, the sex was great. She and I had a comfortable ebb and flow when it came to BDSM, and being with her had allowed me to explore a side of myself I'd never before known. Finding out who I was and owning my identity had somehow healed a part of me that had been wounded for years. No matter what would happen between us, I had Brooke to thank for that gift. But I wasn't feeling as strongly about our relationship anymore, not since her betrayal in the bar and other mind games and gaslighting techniques she used on my psyche. She'd apologized and we had talked about it, but I couldn't wrap my head around how someone could supposedly love me and also choose to embarrass or publicly tease me. I never again wanted to feel that way, and I knew I'd taken a couple of steps backward in my willingness to trust someone with my feelings.

I watched Brooke as she wandered through my home and looked at my family's belongings. I knew Naomi would be furious if she knew another woman was inside her private domain, her personal sanctuary, the home where she'd raised her children. Brooke slowly meandered through the rooms, picking up framed photos, looking at artwork, running her hands across furniture, and sitting in some of the rooms as she looked around. I knew she was comparing herself to my wife, just as any woman would do. For a fleeting moment, I felt I should defend Naomi or protect her from whatever unkind thoughts or opinions Brooke might be forming as she stared at my wife's photos.

"We should probably get going soon," I suggested. "Are you hungry?"

"In a few minutes. Let me just finish looking around. This is a big house, but I could take care of it, I'm sure. And you know I'm a great cook. You always love my cooking. I could whip you up some great meals in that kitchen!"

I felt like telling her to send me her resume and I'd call her for an interview when I was ready for a new wife. It was true Brooke was indeed a very good cook. She had cooked plenty of great meals for me. But I wasn't a fool. Being married, running a house, and raising kids is different.

"Well, now you can tell your friends you've been to my house anyway, right? That should satisfy them."

She leaned against a wall and sucked her cheek as she stared, long and hard, at one of my sofas. I watched expectantly to see what would happen next. Finally, she uncrossed her arms and threw them into the air.

"You know what's wrong with this room, Alex?"

"I didn't know anything was wrong it."

"Well, there is. The longer sofa should face the door, not have its back toward it. When people are seated on it, they can't feel safe if their backs are toward the door. It's a fact, a proven fact."

"I'll get right on that, but can we go get something to eat, please?"

"Seriously, Alex, in the most abstract form, there's a dialectical tension in this room. Socrates and Plato studied dialectical tension, but it wasn't until the 1980s that it emerged in materialistic modes like what I'm talking about. Dialectical tensions are usually studied as a system comprised of two incompatible items or beings—"

"Come on, Doctor Freud; you can psychoanalyze me over a good steak," I said as I grabbed her arm and steered her to the door.

I was suddenly overcome with a burning desire to place a ball gag into Brooke's mouth. Forget the canes. Forget the whips. I'd have done anything to get my hands on my suitcase full of tools and toys so I could save myself. I'd begun to prefer Brooke when she was quiet and submissive. Her know-it-all attitude was coming out more and more frequently, it seemed.

We went to a steakhouse and had an early dinner, and although we could have gone right back to Brooke's house, we had sex in my truck first. With her right leg sticking up through my sunroof and the left one braced against my passenger seat's headrest, I was soon reminded of why I tolerated the woman's incessant need to shrink everyone and everything around us. Plus, an hour later, as I drove us to her house, she treated me to the oral skills I preferred. Since her son was home, Brooke and I straightened our clothes, brushed our hair, and then walked into her house.

"There's a leftover ribeye in the fridge, whenever you feel like it," she told her son through his closed bedroom door.

"Hey! *Your* damned sofa doesn't face your front door either! Is this a Freudian slip or what?" I laughed as I sat down in her living room and grabbed the TV remote.

"*My* living room isn't big enough for that option."

"Well, you will be punished later for giving me hell about my decorating efforts when yours are no better. Prepare for your punishment, woman; it's coming."

"I like the sound of that."

CHAPTER 9

UNTOLD KINK

Over dinner one night, Brooke and I talked about our recent afternoon's sex play. As we sat in a curved booth and shared our second bottle of Cabernet, she said, "It never occurred to me how much I'd love being restrained in a straitjacket." An older, white-haired woman in choker pearls looked over from the nearby table at us, wide-eyed and shocked. Her mouth was agape, and her hand was on her chest as she leaned away from her table. Obviously, the balding gentleman to her left hadn't heard Brooke's comment as he calmly sipped his Scotch. Brooke and I dissolved into laughter as I poured her more wine from the decanter on our table, even before the waiter could get back to do it.

Brooke took a sip, winked at me, and continued. "I'm moist again, just thinking about how it felt as you buckled me into the jacket. I got so excited as my breath caught and I felt the collar against my throat and the cold metal ring on my flesh. I'd had no idea earlier in the week when you'd called and asked me measurements so you could order a straitjacket for me! But when the box showed up and I opened it and saw what was inside, I could hardly wait to put it on! I'll admit I rubbed it against myself and couldn't wait for you to get to my house!"

The prim and proper woman at the nearby table looked over at us again. This time she put down her fork, her breast heaving as she tried to show her distaste. She pushed away from the table and stormed off to the ladies' room in her two-piece Chanel suit. "Let me go and enlighten her," Brooke said as she slid from our booth.

"Sir, would you like another bottle of Caymus?" our server asked five minutes later as I continued to eat my filet.

"Sure, thank you."

A few minutes later, Brooke came back and slid beside me again. She was grinning a devilish grin as she sipped from her refilled wineglass. I waited to hear what she'd done.

"Okay, what did you do?" I finally asked.

"While Tight-Ass Tilly powdered her nose, I went into the Ladies' Lounge and told her how amazing it is to be bound and commanded by a man who knows what he's doing. I explained how I had gasped in anticipation when you'd instructed that I should outstretch my arms and hold my wrists together so you could buckle them securely. Tight-Ass Tilly tried to act shocked, but when I stopped talking, she pleaded for me to tell her more. So, I went on and explained how my breath had caught when you'd cinched my waist from behind and folded my arms across my waist in front, comfortably underneath my breasts. I told her how my nipples were erect and begging for more as you securely buckled the straitjacket and then tightened the leg straps at my crotch. Tilly licked her lips when I told her I wore no panties and I was so wet and waiting, helpless and exposed, but desperate for your touch. She begged for me to tell her the whole thing!"

I laughed and took a sip of my wine and so did Brooke. "Does that woman need medical attention now?" I asked. "Oh, no! Quite the contrary," said Brooke, laughing.

"What's that mean?"

"I showed her this."

She opened her handbag to show me the silky panties inside. "I told her she needs to step up her game with her man, that she needs to live a little." Just then, Tight-Ass Tilly came back into the dining room in her proper Chanel suit. Her pink lipstick had been reapplied and she had a twinkle in her eye as she walked toward her table. Her husband rose to pull her chair out for her. When he sat down again, she picked up her clutch handbag from the table, opened it, and let him have a look inside. The old man's face lit up and he signaled the waiter for their check. Then he quickly emptied his Scotch glass. Brooke and I cracked up.

Brooke and I had indeed enjoyed a great afternoon the previous day. She'd made a willing submissive and she had thoroughly enjoyed the straitjacket, desperate to please me. There was nothing she wouldn't do for me. When I'd spun the D-ring at the collar and made her look at herself in the mirror, I'd known she was mine. Her eyes had told me so since she couldn't speak, thanks to her damp panties I'd put into her mouth. I'd worn a leather-spiked mask for our sex play, and Brooke had begged me to enter every part of her and know her on every level. She was mine in every sense. As she sat beside me in the restaurant, I realized I'd never known anyone on such an intimate level, no one, not even the mother of my children. I owned the woman next to me, inside and out, every pore, every crevice, every molecule. The power I held was inebriating beyond anything I'd ever known or felt.

After hours of taking her, owning her, and making her submissive to my every whim, I had released Brooke from her chains and leather cuffs. It was time for us to shower and dress for a cocktail party. She felt better. I felt fantastic, indomitable, even. As we'd showered together, she'd proceeded to shave my black and white tattoos very gently, removing all of the hair that might make them look dirty or unkempt; then she shaved my bald head nice and neat. She'd told me her head was clear and she felt renewed and refreshed. I felt the same. We'd each received just what we had needed. Bliss—that was the word Brooke had used to describe how she'd felt after our afternoon together. I felt a sense of empowerment that I'd given her bliss and taken her to such new heights. What we'd shared was certainly nothing my wife would have entertained, not in a million lifetimes.

While we'd been at the cocktail party, Brooke couldn't stop staring at me, enamored with me and, somehow, seeing me through new eyes. She seemed to worship, respect, and revere me even more than before. Our souls had connected and intertwined on an elevated plateau, all because she'd been willing to let go and allow me to indulge.

At the cocktail party, and at dinner, Brooke couldn't keep her hands off me. I loved that she needed to touch and feel me, even if only to brush my arm. Just her gaze connected and pulled me in, holding me as if no one else were around. The way she leaned into me to smell my cologne was intoxicating to both of us. She was my soulmate. I had found my soulmate, my one and only soulmate, the one person on the planet who truly got me and understood my every need. It was a huge relief to have found her. When she touched my skin, electricity went from her fingertips into my skin and recharged and invigorated me, giving me renewed energy, a sense of peace.

Was this true passion? Was it love? What was happening to me? Whatever it was, it felt good to be needed, to be wanted.

"What are you thinking about?" Brooke asked as she took my hand and placed it on her thigh.

"Our day."

"Well, you promised we'd still go to the dungeon tonight. The day's not over yet."

She slowly hiked up her skirt so I could feel and see her warm moistness glistening through her sheer panties. Hidden behind the floor-length tablecloth, my fingers slid into her flesh as she stared into my eyes, moaned, and closed her eyes. "Tell me what you'd like to do at the dungeon, you little slut," I said as I enjoyed watching her pleasure. But her lips trembled, and she couldn't speak as her body shuddered under my touch. I laughed at my easy little wench.

When we ordered our meal, we ordered just one large entrée. As the waiter brought the platter, Brooke picked up my set of silverware, handed it to the waiter, and said, "We won't need these, thanks." We'd agreed we weren't hungry enough for two entrées, but I was somewhat hungry. Now Brooke had just given away my fork and knife. I eyed her with curiosity as she moved closer in the booth and then used her fork and knife to begin cutting the filet. As I watched, she raised the forkful with a bite of steak to my mouth as she licked her lips. "For my master," she said. While I chewed, she took a bite for herself and then got another one for me. As she put the next bite to my lips, a woman at the nearby table watched wide-eyed as if in utter shock. Her date, however, seemed to be in awe of my situation. I wrapped my arm around Brooke as she continued to feed me, even dabbing the corner of my lip in between bites. "Wine, sir?" Brooke asked as she handed me my glass. A woman at another table scoffed in disgust as she stared. The man with her looked en-

tirely unfazed as he ate his dessert, but yet, he glanced up, only to
catch my eye, smile, and nod his approval and respect.

I felt extremely gratified in that moment, but not in a sexual
way. Yet I felt satiated on a level like never before. I knew it was a
good thing. It was something I wanted to feel again, for sure. Brooke
fed me my entire meal this way, alternating my bites with her own,
all the way through dessert. It was sexy, alluring, provocative, and a
precursor turn-on for the rest of the evening.

Hours later, we walked into the dungeon club. My suitcase of
toys contained Brooke's favorite new gadgets, including the straitjacket she could hardly wait to wear again, only this time, in public.
Before we went inside, I changed my shirt and put on just a black
vest over my tattooed chest, atop my kilt and shoes. Brooke still
wore her black cocktail dress with cap sleeves, but she'd soon strip
it off, once inside the club. "Woman, slow down!" I laughed as she
hurried inside on her high heels. "We've got all night!"

Her body radiated with anticipation as we went inside and said
hello to the members we knew. Brooke dispensed with the usual
niceties; she didn't even want a bottled water for later. Like a kid
in a candy store, she took my hand and led me to one of the most
prominent display platforms where another couple had just finished
their bondage play. We could tell they were headed upstairs to the
loft for some serious sex because they made a beeline in that direction. "No, I pick," I reminded Brooke, as I walked to another platform that held a spanking bench. She obediently followed as I knew
she would. While I set up my tools, Brooke went to the ladies' room
to change out of her dress.

Ten minutes later, she was back, entirely nude except for a black
thong, black-thigh high stockings, stiletto heels, and the excited grin
she wore. "Wipe that smile off your face, you little slut!" I ordered.

"And cover the bench with a clean sheet!" She obeyed, immediately falling into her submissive role. I wasted no time binding her in her beloved straitjacket. Once she was secured and immobilized, I ordered my submissive to bend over the A-framed spanking bench centered in the middle of the platform. I buckled on her play collar, then the wrist cuffs, and finally the ankle cuffs. Reaching into my bag, I quickly found my lengths of chain to restrain her arms and legs to the bench eyelets. Cinching the chain down nice and tight to where she couldn't move was my specialty. There—all set. Wearing my tight black leather gloves, I lightly flogged her as a few members came over to watch while they sipped their waters and gazed in amusement. As she relaxed and began to feel comfortable, I gave my submissive several unexpected harder lashings that got her attention and raised welts on buttocks and lower thighs. Even in the dim flickering lighting, and without touching her, I saw the glistening wetness between my submissive's legs. I could smell her sexual desire from where I stood; it made me hot, driven to make her soar in subspace. She was in ecstasy already as her head lifted as far back as the D-ring would allow. Lost in our play, we both forgot we were on a stage and others watched. I switched to my favorite bamboo cane and surprised her with a quick wrist flick that stunned her and made her gasp and cry out, but her body shuddered in appreciation as she tried to get her breath again. I knew just how much pressure to apply, just what she liked, just what was enough, but what wouldn't be too much as I raised red welts on her bare ass and the back of her thighs. My goal was to bring blood to the fleshy, meaty areas—not to draw blood, but just to pleasurably warm those spots. A few unexpected cane flicks did the trick while keeping my submissive from entirely slipping into a foggy subspace. I carefully watched her reactions and gauged my pressure and intensity to keep her on the heady rollercoaster and maintain control over her ride as she moaned for more. When her eyes glazed over, I knew she'd gone over the ledge into that deep erotic abyss. She was mine—entirely, wholly, mine. But she was ready for more; she craved more, so much more. I had only warmed her up.

I grabbed a short length of chain and connected it to the D-ring on the back of her collar. She knew what was coming next. Out of my bag I grabbed an ass hook. Oh, the curved hook with the stainless steel ball on the end…perfect. With a little lube on my finger, I circled her anus, getting ready to insert the hook and draw the chain tight to connect the top of the hook. Snap. Ahh, there, nice and firm; that will keep her mind busy. I put a ball gag in her pretty little mouth, just so the dungeon monitor wouldn't be too worried with the loud moans of total ecstasy about to emanate from her. As my submissive looked away from me, I picked up my favorite leather whip and brought it down hard. I let it crack onto the bare flesh of her pink ass cheeks. Oh, the rush that came over me. Over the music and through the ball gag, her screams were muffled as her mind scrambled to decipher pain from pleasure. But before her clear answer could be assimilated, the next lashing kissed her glowing red hot ass and tears ran down her cheeks as her head fell forward, pulling the ass hook deeper. Positioned in my true form, leaning in with my left arm behind my back, I precisely whipped her pink ass like a professional rodeo whip cracker.

After a dozen or so cracks of the whip, I walked up to her and rubbed her beautiful, now marked, ass. "Do you know who your master is?" I whispered in her ear as I held back her disheveled hair from the side of her face.

She couldn't answer, couldn't even focus on me. She blinked her eyes ever so slowly. Her blank stare told me she knew. I'd given her what she'd wanted, what she had needed, and somewhere amid the tangle of pain and pleasure, we had both found what we'd been seeking. As I unchained her, she fell limp into my arms. I removed the restrictive straitjacket from her trembling, sweaty form. She couldn't stand. She was unable to speak. I wrapped the sheet around her naked body, and I helped her to a nearby sofa. She lay still and silent while I picked up our toys and wiped down the spanking bench for the next couple's playtime. When I'd finished, I gave Brooke a sip of water and held her close, still wrapped in the sheet.

"Want to go upstairs?" I whispered.

She tried to stand, but her unsteady legs shook like a newborn foal. I helped her up and then supported her as we slowly made our way up to the loft. For a while, I quietly held her as we lay on a beanbag bed in a darkened area of the loft, away from anyone else, in a private space. She seemed cold, so I pulled a fur throw over her and wrapped my arm around her.

"I love you," she finally managed. "Thank you for giving me just what I needed, for being my master, for taking me to those heights. Only you can take care of my needs. Only you know me, and now I understand your power, Alexander. Now I know the real you." She was right. I knew her. She knew me. No one knew me like she did. No one trusted me like she trusted me. I'd finally found my soulmate. As I made love to her, while growling in her ear, I held on to that knowledge, safe in my new identity as a dominant, the man I was meant to be.

There was so much power just in knowing myself, the person I'd carried around inside my façade for decades! I felt like I could do anything, be anything, surmount any obstacle, find any success, and create any reality from any dream! Yet I still had that reality waiting at home, that very real thing called my wife, the woman I'd vowed to love, honor, and respect for all eternity. When I thought of Naomi, it was like someone dumped a bucket of ice water on me and made me shake off that other life I'd been living, like someone tapped me on the shoulder and said, "Hey, buddy, it's um, Reality, here, just checking in. Can I have a moment?"

Sure, I had moved into a separate room in our home, and I had furnished it with my man furnishings to make it my own. I had even enjoyed plenty of freedom, time, and space. Naomi had busied herself with other activities, her job, our kids, our grandkids, and chosen to lose herself in her iPad. But she wasn't blind, not at all. In time, my wife did her research like a murder detective to check up on just where her husband would go and what he'd do with his time. When it all came to a head one day, I didn't deny her suspicions were founded. After twenty-six years, it wouldn't have been right for me to keep up the lie. She was the mother of our children. She deserved that much.

"Why? I just want to know why?" she demanded.

"I was just bored with life, with me, with us, with everything. The pressure and chaos of the life we have both created was just too overwhelming"

"So, you think it's my damned job to entertain you for the duration of our marriage? I failed to entertain you—that's the problem?"

"Something was lacking; that's all, Naomi."

"Something's lacking between your ears."

I wasn't proud I'd hurt her, and just the realization of my actions made me want to die. It had never been my intention to create such hurt in a woman who loved me so much. But what came next was something I never could have expected, not in a million years. "Well, how long's it going to take for you to get this shit out of your system?" she asked.

"What? What do you mean?" I asked.

"This midlife crisis crap," she said. "How long will it last?"

"I—I have no—it's not a midlife crisis! Something was lacking that's been missing for years, long before I hit midlife!"

"That's bullshit and you know it! We've got a good life! We have two great kids, and you went and fucked it all up! How long do I have to wait for you to get this through your damned system?" she yelled.

"Look; it's not like fucking *diarrhea*! It's not running through me and I'll get over it when it's all out!"

"Yes, it is! That's exactly what it is! And who is this *slutty* bitch you've been seeing anyway?"

The words "Hell hath no fury" flashed through my mind like a gigantic warning sign that cautioned me not to reveal Brooke's name. Naomi's eyes looked wild with fury. I couldn't have my kids' mother going and doing something we'd all regret, especially when the root of the problem had started with me. "Well?" she demanded. "A name! I want a name!"

"Does it matter? I mean, really?"

"You know I'll find out, Alex! And I guess I should go and get tested for God knows what now! What diseases does this whore have? How many men does she sleep with—because when you bang her, you're with every one of *them*! Thank you! Thanks a lot for exposing me to all that shit, too! And what about our kids? Your son and daughter will lose all respect for you when they hear what you've done! How could you do this to our family, to us, to them? This was so thoughtless!"

Even through her blind rage, she made some sense, I had to admit. It hadn't been my intent to screw up everything. I had simply been feeling unappreciated, lonely, and forgotten. I'd only wanted to feel better and find the real me before I died. For once, I'd wanted to make it about me and about what Alex wanted. Yet we'd tried to raise our kids to be good and honorable people, and here I was, their dad who'd royally screwed it all up. Naomi stormed off and stopped talking to me for a while. I wasn't sure what she was going to do, and to be honest, I wasn't sure what I wanted her to do. I didn't even know what I wanted to do.

. . .

"Going out tonight?" Naomi asked as she walked into my bedroom one Friday evening.

"Uh, yeah." I didn't want to look at her. We hadn't spoken in days, and I was getting ready to go out on a date with Brooke. A weird fog hung over the room, like neither of us should be there about to have a bizarre conversation. The surreal situation couldn't have felt any more awkward as my stomach churned and knotted. With my back to her, I began to button my blue and white striped shirt.

"Well, give me that shirt," she scoffed. "It needs ironing. You can't go out like that."

That imaginary flashing caution sign turned on again inside my head. Was it a trap? I was afraid to turn around. Was my wife standing behind me with a butcher knife, or perhaps an axe? No man's wife offers to iron his shirt for a date with his mistress.

"Hurry up, before I change my mind."

I unbuttoned the shirt and slowly turned around. Slowly, reluctantly, I handed it over. She grabbed it and shook her head as she looked at my pants.

"Seriously? You know those pants are too big on you now that you've lost weight. Put on the black Dockers instead. They fit you much better. And give me that pair. I'm tossing them in the Goodwill bag. You can't wear those anymore."

Before I could say a word, she was gone, and so was my favorite striped shirt. I wondered if she'd gone to shred it with her sewing shears. But I had to leave soon, so I changed into the black Dockers as Naomi had suggested. Five minutes later, as I was putting on a belt, she came back in with the pressed shirt.

"Now you'll look like somebody gives a damn about you. And you see? Those pants fit you much better."

"Uh, thanks."

But I hesitated to take the ironed shirt from her as she stood holding the shirt between us with her arm outstretched. "Well, take the damned shirt! I didn't cover it in ricin powder, for God's sake!"

I had to go. Brooke would be waiting for me. But Naomi's demeanor had totally unnerved me. I had no idea what was happening. I left the house that night thinking all the way down to Brooke's home.

CHAPTER 10

SECRETS REVEALED

I called Brooke the next day to tell her I was sorry for being so distracted last night. So much was going through my mind. In our conversation, I could tell Brooke was thrilled and relieved when I told her about my conversation with Naomi and how she knew the truth about us. Brooke seemed to take the news to mean she'd more quickly move toward becoming my wife. That was not, however, how my wife saw things, not even close.

"I'll wait her out," Naomi had told me. "I love you, Alex. I took vows, and I intend to honor those vows. Besides, how many times have I told you how my parents' divorce hurt me, and how it screwed up my sister's life and my own? There's no way I'll ever do that to our kids! You screwed up, but I refuse to punish our kids because you can't keep your damned dick inside your pants. Get it all out of your system, and then we'll go on with our marriage like it's supposed to be."

"She said *what*?" Brooke exclaimed. "That's crazy, Alex! Didn't you tell her that we're in love? People don't get **over** *being in love*! Our dynamic is amazing in this lifestyle we've found together. I can see us explore this relationship and our kink together forever! I am your devoted submissive, and you are my sir; that goes deeper than anything and on so many levels. Did you tell her *that*?"

"We'll talk about it later. I'll come by your house after work. I've got a client coming to my office in a few minutes. I need to go over his contract before he arrives. I'll see you later."

"But Alex! No, wait a damned minute! Hold on! Did you tell her she's *got to go*?"

"Bye, Brooke. Later."

I had no one coming by my office. I just needed the incessant nagging to stop. Brooke was, in her mind, already in the wife position in our relationship. All that needed to happen was for Naomi to be ejected from that spot, as if spouses were interchangeable pawns in the Game of Life. That was Brooke's interpretation of the issue, anyhow. Brooke's son would soon leave for college, and my daughter would soon do the same. In Brooke's mind, she had already moved into my lakefront home, and she and I would naturally become the lord and lady of the manor as she'd ease into my life once Naomi was out. She was, in fact, jubilant that Naomi had learned about her existence. She couldn't have been happier.

For the next two hours, I both *wanted* Brooke and felt consumed by dread, unsure what I should do that evening, *or* for the rest of my life. The smooth white stone paperweight stared at me from atop my desk, a reminder of the day when I had disappeared from reality and played hooky. I picked up the stone and rolled it in my palm. With my eyes shut, I conjured recollections of salty air, warm sun, gentle breezes, and the rhythmic sounds of the water as it had lapped at the shoreline. Another time, another place, another person—that's what that day had been. Why couldn't I always be as relaxed and carefree as I'd felt on that day? Why couldn't I feel as fulfilled and whole as that day had let me be? Escapism was a glorious gift, almost like a magical reset button for my sanity, I realized. But was that all Brooke had been, simply an escape, or a temporary departure from life's stresses?

A text alert from my cell phone interrupted my thoughts. It was Brooke, I saw: ***Master, your obedient whore is ready and waiting, with every trembling orifice quivering and eager to receive you.*** The woman had a way with words. I smiled as I replaced the stone on my desktop, shut down my computer, and grabbed my truck's keys. "See you in the morning, Marcie," I told our receptionist as I passed by her desk.

As I drove toward Brooke's house, I felt the growing urgency inside my pants. That was the difference in steering my truck toward Brooke's home versus my own. At my home, when I walked inside the door, I knew to expect the same old monotony. Nothing would change. The evening would be anticlimactic and uneventful, and most likely, painfully boring. If my daughter were there, she'd be on her electronics, buried in social media, or else getting ready to go out somewhere, with no time for Dad. I understood that, of course, but it didn't make it any better. Naomi, on the other hand, was my wife; and she'd had zero interest in me before she had learned I'd strayed outside our marriage, desperate for companionship. In earlier days, when she and I did have sex, it had been so predictable I could have set my watch by it. There was nothing exciting, fun, or exhilarating about it. We had a goal. We accomplished it. Game over.

Sex with Brooke meant playful excitement and new discoveries. She always allowed me carte blanche to do whatever I chose, and however I chose. There were no rules and no restrictions. I was always in charge, entirely in control of the whole show and what we did. Instead of feeling like an overlooked, unimportant burden in my own home, I was the king of the castle in Brooke's home. Whatever I said was law. Whatever I wanted was respected. Whatever I required was delivered.

This day was no different. I parked my truck in Brooke's driveway, got out, and waved at her neighbor who, by now, regarded me as Brooke's longtime boyfriend since he'd seen me at her house so often. I knew as I put my key in her front door that Brooke's son was out of town on a camping trip with friends, so we had the house to ourselves. As soon as I opened the door, delicious aromas wafted from the kitchen. Brooke was an excellent cook, and she often made meals for me when I visited. But on this evening, I needed to feed a hunger of a different kind before I could eat dinner.

"Why are you wearing clothes?" I asked as I grabbed her hair from behind and pushed my body firmly against hers, pinning her against the kitchen counter. As I firmly twisted the handful of hair at the nape of her neck, she moaned and leaned into me, happy that I'd arrived—and happier to feel the urgent bulge that pressed against her ass.

"I thought we'd eat first. I've got a pot roast cooking for you."

I turned her around and wholly, fully kissed her on her mouth, tasting every corner and every recess. She hungrily explored my mouth with her tongue and wrapped her arms around me. As we kissed, I tore at her blouse, and in one motion, I ripped it from her, leaving her heaving, bra-covered breasts still covered. When she reached behind her back to unhook her bra, I grabbed her hands and held them behind her, but I continued to kiss her. I took a pair of scissors from the nearby butcher-block knife holder on the countertop, stopped kissing her, and looked down into her eyes. She trusted me fully. We both knew it. I ran the scissors down her chest, then down the side of her left breast as she moaned with urgency. As she watched, I inserted the metal end of the scissors between her cleavage, snipped her bra, and released her breasts. I lightly dragged the cold metal blade on her breasts as she stood perfectly still; and then I leaned down and sucked hard on her nipple until she winced in pain. I put down the scissors and kissed her again, deeply, passionately, fully, as her bare breasts rubbed against my shirt.

"Take off those pants!" I ordered. She didn't hesitate. In a split-second, her shorts lay on the tiled floor as she stood in front of me and awaited my next command. "And the panties, whore!" I stood back and looked at her, up and down, really looked at her. She was a typical middle-aged woman, nothing remarkable, not from a physical standpoint, anyway. Her body had born a child. She could have stood to drop a few pounds. Even a tan would have enhanced her skin's appearance. Gravity had found her, like it finds most women her age. But at the same time, Brooke was my soulmate, the singular woman, the sole person on the planet whom I'd been destined to find. I took comfort in that fact as I stared at my perfectly imperfect mistress, the one person who seemed to really understand me, and the woman who let me do to her anything I wanted.

"Should we go into my—" she began.

But I cupped my hand over her face, just hard enough to get her attention and remind her of who was in control. "Do not speak unless spoken to," I ordered. "Wait here." I left her standing naked in her kitchen while I poured myself a whiskey on the rocks. Then I sat down at her kitchen table and slowly drank it as I watched her. She was uncomfortable I knew. Her discomfort then went to ire. I saw it in the fury in her eyes. I knew her well enough to know she was moist and her heart was racing as she awaited me. When I'd emptied my glass, I left it on the kitchen table. Then I went back to Brooke.

"On your knees!"

Wordlessly, she dropped before me as I undid my belt and then my pants. I was so hard it was difficult to release my cock from my pants. "Do what you do best, you slut." Brooke took me into her mouth, fully and skillfully working her magic like an obedient submissive. In no time, I grasped her head, pulled her to me, and yelled out. But I wasn't done with her yet. I picked Brooke up, sat her atop the island in her kitchen, and licked her moist sweetness completely. She moaned as she spread her legs and hung onto the sides of the island countertop.

"Please, sir; please!" she begged. "Please give it to me!"

I loved for her to beg, to know how much she wanted and craved me. She arched her hips and pleaded some more, unable to contain herself. I stood up, pulled her to the island's edge, and then all at once, thrust hard and deep into her pulsating wetness. Without stopping, I thrust harder and faster, and Brooke hung onto me until she screamed out as her body shook. She tried to catch her breath, but I wasn't far behind and continued the rhythmic pumping into my little whore until her master's juices spilled from her.

"I hope there's homemade mashed potatoes with that pot roast," I told her.

"Just as you like, sir," Brooke smiled as she sat up and slid off the island countertop.

· · ·

The tension in our house somewhat subsided over time. Our son had learned of my dalliance and was royally pissed at me. Our daughter was irritated, but she was busy with her own teenage angst so that gave me some breathing room about my transgressions, for the time being, at least. But I was unsure what was going on with

Naomi. That uncertainty made me nervous since I didn't know what to expect, how she felt about what I'd done, or what was the state of our marriage. Weirder still was Naomi's attitude toward my continued dating life.

"Date Night tonight?" Naomi asked on a Saturday as she unloaded the dishwasher when I walked into the kitchen.

I looked behind me, at first expecting to see our son. "Oh, uh, I guess so, yeah," I stammered.

"Well, you'd better let me trim the back of your neck for you. Meet me in the bathroom. I'll get the electric clipper."

The caution lights began to flash. All the warning bells sounded. Was that *it*? Did she plan to cut my throat? She was far too calm, much too reserved. This was not the Naomi I knew. What in the hell was going on?

"So, where are you two going tonight?" Naomi asked as she slowly moved the electric clipper across the back of my hairline. "Uh, dinner, just dinner," I replied. I didn't want to give her any reason to feel more hurt or even further betrayed by me. I didn't want her to sit around and ache for the husband out cheating on her. But it was beyond bizarre that my wife was discussing my evening plans with me, knowing full well I was about to be with my mistress. Somehow, she took a bit of the fun out of the equation for me. Her overly passive demeanor really threw me, and it irritated the hell out of me.

"Hey, you want to hear something funny?" she asked.

"What's that?" I asked, although I couldn't imagine anything funny that could possibly come from her mouth in that moment.

"Well, you know all those times I was on my iPad? I was upstairs looking at bondage porn."

"What?" I jerked around and stared at her.

"Don't do that! Do you want me to shave a big runway into your head?" she asked.

"You mean, you were upstairs looking at bondage porn and I was downstairs talking to women about the same thing?" Nothing could have shocked me more.

"Yep, that's right," she said.

I shook my head and looked at her reflection in the mirror. "Naomi! Why didn't you ever tell me?"

"Why didn't you ever tell *me*?" she asked. "You could've told me you were into that stuff."

"So, what's with all this nice girl crap now? Why are you being tolerant of me seeing Brooke?"

"Oh, I'm just waiting for you to get your head out of your ass," she said. "Now, you'd better hurry or you'll be late. She's waiting for you."

As I drove to meet Brooke, I thought about how Naomi had spent time looking at bondage porn. How had I never known she'd been interested in it? Or, I wondered, had Naomi only told me that as a way to keep the door open to our twenty-six-year marriage? Like my wife's unconventional new attitude to my extramarital affair, her newfound interest in bondage porn had also hit me out of nowhere. Again, things weren't making sense for me.

Brooke continuously pried for details about how things were going at home and how Naomi had been acting. She was desperate for any new information that might give her a sign my wife was ready to let me go and let go of our marriage so she could move in. But Naomi had a lot on the line after two decades, and not just for herself. Her kids' lives mattered to her as well; she didn't want to spin their minds with over-guessing that this could have been their fault and shatter the lives they'd always known. It was bad enough our kids knew I'd cheated on their mother and our marriage was going through a rocky time. But Naomi was steadfast in her resolve to wait Brooke out.

· · ·

Maybe I was feeling my newfound power. Maybe I wanted to take my dominant role to the next level. Even I couldn't be sure why I did some of the things I chose to do. But one thing was sure: I liked the new Alexander and I never wanted to let him go.

One night, after hours of rough sex play, I wanted to keep my dominant control going even after I left Brooke alone and begging for more. I wanted more, even after I returned home to my other life. I had already begun to experiment with just how far my reach over Brooke could extend. "Have you had anything to drink, even a single glass of wine?" I asked her. "No, sir, not a drop since you told me to stop drinking it and to pay strict attention to my diet. No, sir; no wine, nothing. I wouldn't dare disobey you, not ever."

We lay together under a thick down comforter, relaxed and tired, as we talked for a while. "Tell me about something that makes you uncomfortable," I said, "something you fear." I felt with certainty that her answer would have something to do with body image and how she felt about herself and her figure. Like many women her age, Brooke wasn't happy with her appearance. Being in public at the club was something she risked only because of the payoff she'd received. Yet she'd never felt proud of her appearance nor sexy as a woman. She looked down, swallowed hard, and said, "I've always felt so uncomfortable with my looks, my body. You know? I even have this weird recurring dream where I'm standing totally naked as all these gloved hands—they're blue medical gloves—come at me and point out all my flaws and imperfections. It goes on and on, forever, and I feel humiliated as if many eyes are judging me and picking apart everything about me. In the dream, I feel ashamed. But it gets even worse, the hands lay me down and begin probing me, inside my mouth, between my legs, inside my vagina. I'm as imperfect inside as on the outside. When I wake from those dreams, I have the worst days. I'm an absolute wreck; I just shake for the whole day, and I can't even look at myself in a mirror. I've never told anyone that before."

"Okay, let's see if we can work on that," I told her.

"What's that mean?"

"You'll have to trust me."

"I trust you, sir, completely."

Since Naomi knew all about Brooke, there was no need to continue the ruse that I went to friends' homes anymore. That also opened the door to allowing myself to stay overnight at Brooke's home. Some mornings, I woke up at Brooke's, showered, went straight to the office, and then returned to Brooke's in the evening.

"Today is Panty-Free Tuesday," I told Brooke one morning over breakfast.

"What?" she laughed. But she saw I wasn't laughing.

"For you, that is. Today is a no-panty day for you. You will go to work without panties under your skirt and no pantyhose either, nothing under the skirt."

"Yes, sir, as you wish." She got up, removed my empty plate, and placed it in the kitchen sink.

Since she'd already dressed for the office, Brooke reached underneath her knee-length navy skirt and slipped off her light blue lace panties as I watched. "Come here," I instructed. "I'll take those." I slipped her panties into my shirt pocket and then ran my hand up her thigh and into her warm, moist recesses. Her legs instantly parted as she sank into my hand and pulled my head toward her breast as I sat beside her. I gently stroked her, careful not to give her too much pleasure.

"You'll be late," I said. "Go to work and I'll call you later."

"I can be a few minutes late."

"Did I stutter? Go to work."

"Yes, sir."

After she left, I locked up Brooke's house and then headed to my own office. It was a weird feeling to go to work from Brooke's home instead of from my family home, but I'd already done it quite a few times, by now, still unsure of where I belonged. An unsettled feeling had come over me in recent weeks. I'd once thought Naomi and I would figure things out and do what was best for our family. But now, I felt lost and more confused than ever. All I'd ever wanted was to feel appreciated, loved, and important to my wife. Yet I'd looked outside my marriage for what I hadn't found at home, and what had resulted were even more problems than those I'd first faced.

CHAPTER 11

BLURRED LINES

"Are you *really* going to the National Design Expo?" Naomi asked as she watched me pack one morning. "What? Yeah, that's where I'm going. It's in Las Vegas. You can check. It runs Friday through Sunday. That's why I want to get there tonight and get checked in and registered."

She walked closer and took out the folded shirts I'd haphazardly put into my suitcase. She then refolded all six of them and neatly replaced them. They looked exactly the same to me, but she felt better.

"Look, Naomi; I don't want you to drive yourself crazy all the time."

"*I* am not driving myself crazy; let's get that straight! *I* have not done anything! This is all *your* doing!"

She was right. It hadn't been her fault, but she was the one still suffering. She was the one who had to watch me as I came and went and lived a life outside of our marriage. She was the one whose heart broke because she had no idea where I was or what I was doing. She was the one who couldn't sleep because she had no clue what the future held for her life or for me for that matter. I'd never felt like a bigger ass as my wife carefully lined up the creases in my dress slacks, folded them, and dutifully placed them in my suitcase. By comparison, I realized some might think she cared more for those damned pants than I cared for her, the mother of my children, the woman I'd promised to love, honor, and protect. Maybe I was an ass. I was so confused in that moment.

"Thanks. I need to get going. My flight is at 1:40." I zipped my suitcase closed and then grabbed my jacket from a nearby chair. "I'll be home on Monday."

I knew she wanted me to kiss her goodbye, but I couldn't do it after I'd just given her a few half-truths. It pained me to see Naomi looking so bad. The stress wore on her. I knew she hadn't been sleeping. It showed in the lines on her face and the constant sadness in her eyes. She had long since cried out most of her tears and exhausted her anger. What remained within her was a dull numbness as she waited to see what I would do next and how my decisions would affect the rest of her life. It wasn't fair to her, and we both knew it.

After I'd left the house, it would be totally still and quiet. The kids were gone for the day, busy with their own activities and interests. As I drove toward the airport, I tried to shake the image from my mind of Naomi, alone and sad, wandering through our family home, stopping to look at family photos and mementos of happier times. Guilt wore heavily on me. I'd never set out to hurt her. As I drove, a song came on the radio that took me back to the last time I'd been in Vegas with Brooke. The music shook me out of my melancholy stupor as I remembered that night....

Brooke had accompanied me that time as well. The Expo had been at the same place a year earlier, in fact. One night, I'd finished dressing early and Brooke had needed a bit more time. "I'll go down to the bar and have a drink. Take your time and just meet me when you're ready," I'd told her. A half-hour later, as I'd sat watching people play the slots, Brooke walked into the bar. I spotted her before she saw me. She looked sexy in a shiny black low-cut blouse with bare shoulders atop a black skirt and black and silver heels. When she noticed me at the end of the bar, she walked toward me. I saw a couple of guys checking her out.

"Is this seat taken?" she asked, winking.

"Not anymore," I joked. "I was holding it, but as hot as you look, it's all yours. Sit down and I'll buy you a drink!"

The bartender came right over as soon as he saw someone. "What may I get for the lady?" he asked as he placed a cocktail napkin on the bar.

"I'll have a Boulevardier, please," Brooke told him as she placed her purse on the bar and got comfortable in the tall, upholstered barstool.

"Yes, ma'am. It'll be just a moment. Another whiskey, sir?" he asked me. I nodded to him to go ahead and bring me one.

I'd grown used to Brooke's signature drink, her damned Boulevardier. I wondered if she even liked the concoction or she just ordered it because she thought it made her appear upscale and sophisticated. I could always tell she liked how the syllables rolled off her tongue when she ordered it. It was one of two of her favorite go-to drinks. Brooke had once told me the cocktail was the creation of an American-born writer who founded a Parisian magazine, also called Boulevardier, that was in publication from 1927 to 1932. It was just my opinion, but I'd thought she liked it because it appeared decadent, and in her mind, a cocktail the wealthy would prefer.

We drank our drinks and continued our pretend cat-and-mouse roleplay game as we joked and teased one another for a little while. After a bit, she placed her hand on my thigh and suggestively ran it up my leg as she looked into my eyes. "Are you in town for long?" she asked as she leaned in toward my ear. "There's supposed to be a meteor shower tonight that's not to be missed. I hear it's supposed to be explosive."

"Got everything you need with you to go for a drive?" I asked as I stood up and threw a fifty on the bar. "I've got a convertible here at the hotel."

Brooke followed my lead and I took her hand. We went out to the valet stand and I had my rental car brought around, a Mustang convertible. "Put the top down for you, sir?" the valet asked from inside the driver's seat, as soon as he'd pulled the car up beside us.

"Please, that'd be great," I said as I pulled a twenty from my pocket for his tip.

Brooke went around to the passenger's side and another valet opened her door for her while I got behind the wheel. It was getting late, but we'd have just enough time to drive up into the hills and find a nice spot from which to watch the meteor shower. We'd already planned to watch the meteor shower so I'd already entered a location into my cell phone and, therefore, knew the general location we'd be headed. I pulled the car onto the road as Brooke settled in and ran one hand through her hair, while adjusting the radio with the other.

When I braked for a traffic light in front of one of the main casinos, I turned to her and said, "Remove your panties."

"What?" she laughed.

"Now. Do it, now. Remove your panties *now*!"

Just as the light turned green, she reached under her skirt and pulled down her panties. Then she pulled them over her high heels and removed them. As I drove us, first through the city, and then onto the highway, I ran my right hand up her thigh and into her warm moistness. She reclined her seat and lay back as I teased and titillated. Warm summer breezes blew through her hair as her eyes rolled back in pleasure. Brooke's hips urgently gyrated and arched to meet my hand as her moans and the radio's music filled the car. No matter what cars or trucks we passed, Brooke made no attempts to pull her skirt down. She didn't want me to stop. As I drove up into the foothills, I looked for a side road.

Finally, I found one and turned down it, toward what appeared to be a cattle ranch. I steered the car toward a tree line, and then shut off the engine. I got out, walked around to the passenger's door, and opened it.

"Get out."

"What?" she asked. "We're in the middle of—"

"Get out *now*!"

When she stood up, I took her hand and led her toward the front of the car. As she struggled to keep her stiletto heels from sinking into the grassy ground, I undid my belt and then my pants. Without a word, I spun her around, bent her over the hood, and plunged deep and hard into the wet recesses that had been driving me mad. Harder and harder I pounded as Brooke lay flat against the hood and the whole car shook back and forth. As if choreographed like some Broadway play, I exploded inside of her just as the meteor show began to rain down above us. But I was still hard as a rock, and not about to waste that moment. How many times do you see a meteor shower? And how many times do you get to have sex under one? So, I went at it a few more times, until Brooke couldn't stand and was begging me to stop.

That was the *last* time we'd been to Vegas. The rigid thickness inside my jeans, as I drove to the airport now, made me hopeful I'd have another sporadic dominant moment on *this* trip as well.

Forty minutes later, my truck's tires squealed as I rounded the inclined ramp into the airport parking garage and then found parking on the third level. I grabbed my suitcase from the backseat and then headed toward the elevator and into the tunnel that connected to the terminal. I wished I felt better, happy even, as I went into the trip. Although I had high hopes for some wild, unbridled sex, something still didn't feel right.

"*There's* my master!" Brooke said as I walked into the terminal's security area. "Right on time, as usual!"

Brooke slung her arms around my neck and kissed me. As I held her, I felt better. "Do we have time for me to get an espresso?" she asked.

"That depends. Did you obey my request?"

"As always, sir. No panties under this skirt, just as you wish, sir."

I shook off the notion that no panties was becoming a theme with us, and I reached to take her carry-on bag from her. We then walked toward the nearby Starbucks. Minutes later, as we sat at a small bistro table, I watched the busy flurry of bustling male travelers passing us.

"Penny for your thoughts," said Brooke, smiling.

"Nothing, nothing at all," I replied. But the truth was I was wondering if any of those other men had screwed up their lives as badly as I'd screwed up my own.

· · ·

When we got to Vegas, we checked in to our hotel and then shared a brief intense sexual encounter, just to wet our appetites for the weekend. After just walking in the door, I followed Brooke into the room and pushed her forward onto the bed. My hands fell behind her knees as my face plunged between her thighs. I could smell her sex just waiting for me to take her and ravage her with my tongue. I eagerly stripped her in haste. I devoured her dripping wet pussy from behind. Making her squirm was my specialty as I rubbed my goatee up and down. After I had fully made her beg for more, I reached down, pulled her hips up to my waist, and then ripped my belt from my pants. The slapping noise of the belt sliding out of my belt loops made her even more horny and wet with anticipation. Looping my belt through the buckle made for the perfect reins. I reached up and firmly placed the belt around her neck as if I were rigging up an unbroken mare for the first ride. As the belt tightened about her neck, I could hear the moans of extreme bliss escape her lips. She pushed her wetness tight up against me and begged me to ride her hard. As I pulled the belt strap with my right hand and slapped her ass with my left hand, I could feel her climax. I knew it was going to be a good trip with this kind of start. I had brought along handcuffs, floggers, and canes, a new powerful ten-speed vibrator that promised to take its user to new pleasure heights, and, of course, her favorite leather cuffs. But since I had to register for the expo and attend a members' dinner at 7:00 p.m., I had to watch the time.

"Do you want to come to dinner tonight?" I asked Brooke.

"I'd rather stay behind and take a bubble bath, order room service, and await my master's return, but I'll do whatever you want."

"No, that's fine. You go ahead and relax and freshen up. I'll just put in an appearance, and then I'll be back. I am expecting you to be ready for me when I get back. Clean, horny, and ready to be used."

Hours later, when I returned to our suite, I found Brooke fast asleep. I let her sleep and climbed into bed to join her. Bing! Tossing and turning all night, I rolled over and looked at my phone, only to see it was 4 a.m. and the only people wide awake were me and my extremely hard pocket rocket. Never missing an opportunity, I rolled over and breathed into her ear and growled. You know the one, the one saying I am going to take you now and devour your soul. Licking the rim of her earlobe, I proceeded down her neck, between her breasts, and straight down to her warm awaiting mound. The more I thought of eating her out, the harder I got. Flinging the covers to the side, I forced her legs apart and dove in for one of my favorite pastimes. Soaking the sheets was my signal to finish the job and take her. Slamming her hips into the mattress for the next hour and a half was amazing. God, how I love spur of the moment sex! Her moans and heavy breathing made my inner beast even more horny, especially in the morning.

The next day, Brooke and I attended the expo in the hotel's grand ballroom. Before dinner, we went into one of the hotel's three bars for a cocktail. I said hello to a few people I recognized, and then Brooke and I found two barstools at the end of the long bar. All day, Brooke had seemed especially clingy. She'd held my hand and remained glued to my side.

"Hey, I left my phone upstairs. Can I borrow yours to call and check on my son?" she asked.

"Yeah, sure. I'm going to the bathroom. Here, you go."

I keyed in my phone's security code and handed her the phone. While I was gone, she made her call.

"Naomi? Hi, Naomi. This is—um, it's Brooke."

Naomi had answered right away, on the first ring, when she'd seen it was my number calling. It must have been like a kick in the gut for her when she heard Brooke's voice, not mine, on the line.

"Brooke? What the—"

"Look, Naomi. Listen; I just wanted to tell you that I love him so much. I love Alex."

"Yeah? Well, I love him, too," Naomi said.

"I just wish he'd hurry up and make a decision."

"Are you…," Naomi hesitated, "are you with him now?"

"Yes."

But before they could talk more, Brooke saw me heading back toward the bar. She told Naomi she needed to go, and she quickly hung up my phone and laid it on the bar.

"Everything good at home?" I asked as I sat down beside her.

"Yeah, all good."

Brooke looked nervous, and suddenly, all at once, I knew why. I picked up my phone and looked to see what number she'd last dialed. "You've got to be the dumbest fucking cunt I've ever met!" I growled through my clenched teeth. "Come here, you, stupid bitch! What have you done?"

I threw a wad of cash down on the bar and then grabbed Brooke's wrist. I hauled her out of the bar, furious that she'd duped me. I didn't care that she'd tried to manipulate *me*, but I was incensed that she'd gone out of her way to hurt Naomi by making sure she knew I was with her. She'd gone too far this time. It had been cruel and downright mean.

"Why did you call Naomi?" I demanded as we rode up to our suite in the elevator.

"Because I love you so much!"

"What the fuck's wrong with you? Better yet, what the fuck is wrong with *me* that I didn't see the *real you*?"

So many questions flooded my mind, but no answers followed any of them. Fatigue soon overwhelmed me, and I felt so smothered in Brooke's presence. I needed to be away from her, just so I could breathe. The walls felt like they were closing in on me. The sight of Brooke sickened me. How could she love me, yet clearly manipulate me and lie to me, not to mention outwardly hurt a woman I still loved? Had I been blinded by lust or by my newfound sexual freedom? And if so, at what cost? What had I done?

"I'm going home. The room's paid for through the weekend. I'm leaving," I said as I threw my clothes in my suitcase.

"Come on, Alex! Please, don't go! I'm sorry! It's just that I love you! I wanted to fight for you; that was all!"

"You crossed the line! You had no right to involve Naomi! That was never your choice to make! How dare you? Know your damned place, woman, and stay in it! And take your fucking hands off of me!"

Brooke jumped as she let go of me, visibly afraid for the first time. She could tell I was furious and meant business. Never before, not when spanked with any of my whips, nor my canes, and not even when she'd been trussed and entirely at my mercy, had Brooke actually felt afraid of me. But now that she had dared to hurt Naomi, she knew real fear—and with good reason. I didn't even look at her again before I walked out of the hotel room.

. . .

When I returned home, Naomi was angry, and I wasn't surprised. She'd taken all she could. She'd ironed my clothes, trimmed my hair, packed my suitcases, and sent me off on my dates. But how much was a woman meant to endure? My wife had reached her breaking point. One of us had to make a move to release us from the chains that bound us. Too much had changed for us to go back. I'd messed everything up, everything I'd ever stood for as a father and a husband. How could I be true to anyone else if I couldn't even be true to myself?

I thought about it long and hard, and then one night, I went home with the forms and said, "Here, Naomi; sign this. We'll come to a mutual decision later on how to split up all our shit."

"Fine." She calmly signed the divorce papers that would ultimately end our marriage. Naomi finally seemed resigned to give in and let go, sure we were no longer salvageable. Maybe she'd had time to process it all and realized our kids were almost young adults who would be able to handle their parents' impending divorce. Or maybe Naomi had finally thrown in the towel and simply surrendered, beaten down and tired of fighting to save a marriage that only one of us seemed to want anymore.

The truth was I couldn't figure out Naomi's motives since I didn't even understand my own decisions at the time. I was still confused as hell and in no shape to make a life-changing decision, especially one of that magnitude. I didn't want to make the wrong move, and certainly not one that would destroy my family. Sleepless nights became the norm for me, and I dragged myself to the office day after day.

"Man, you look like shit!" my brother said one morning.

"That's the nicest thing you've ever said to me. Thanks."

"Those all-night hijinks finally catching up with you?" He laughed as he came into my office and took a seat in front of my desk. "That's why the rest of us do all that crazy stuff in our younger days, when we can handle it!"

"Yeah, I wish. No, it's the stress with Naomi. I'm not sure what I want. I thought I did. One day, I'm ready to move on and get the divorce, but the next.... I don't know if I want to throw away more than twenty-six years and screw it all up."

"Nobody ever said marriage is easy or perfect. And you missed out on a lot in your early years since you guys plunged into it."

"Right, but I feel like I can't live my own truth and be true to anyone if I'm not true to myself. But if I'm true to myself, that means I have to hurt other people, and that makes me a real prick."

"Well, you're a prick, either way, brother," he said, laughing. "So, take that out of the equation."

"You have a point. But here's another thing that's keeping me up at night: Brooke asked to go with me on that upcoming trip I've got scheduled to Hawaii, the trip I won. You remember the one."

"Right, the one from the local supplier, yeah."

"That's the one. Well, Naomi found out somehow that Brooke's supposed to go, too, and that it's not going to be just people from the office."

"But she's known about other things you've done."

"Oh, no. This time is different. Naomi said, in no uncertain terms, that if I board that plane to Hawaii with Brooke, we're done, finished, kaput. 'I am going to stop trying to hold out for you and just let this divorce go through for good.' No more trying to wait this home wrecker out."

"Man, you're really not sure what you want, are you?" my brother asked, suddenly concerned and serious.

"Naomi's been good for so long. She's given me plenty of line and let me explore whatever this thing has been that I've needed to do. But I think she means business this time."

"Yeah, this whole thing was probably a lot more fun when your wife didn't know a damned thing, huh?"

"Maybe, but I've driven her insane, I think. She's skeptical of everyone and everything. Naomi looks for signs and signals in what I do, how I dress, if my preference in food or wine changes, everything. She's pissed at all my friends as if they've led me astray. She thinks my buddies are covering for me and keeping shit from her.

Even if I go get a coffee at Starbucks, she presumes I've gone to some clandestine rendezvous, and by the time I get home, she's got a whole scenario created in her head and has driven herself mad, and it's all my fault for doing that to her."

He shook his head and grimaced. "Yeah, but women are emotional creatures, don't forget, and now they've got the Lifetime Channel and Bravo feeding them scandal and deviancy all damned day. Naomi needs to realize you're probably not half as clever as she gives you credit for, right?"

"You'd be surprised."

"I don't want to know any more than you've already shared. There's some things I just can't un-see from my imagination." He laughed. "Hey, don't forget we've got that meeting with the new clients later today."

"Since when do *you* have to remind *me* of anything?"

"Good point. Get some coffee before the meeting, though. You really do look like shit."

When I was alone again in my office, I opened my photos file on my computer and scrolled to the file that held photos from the day at the shore with Brooke. One by one, I went through sequential shots of the fiery orange sky as it sunk lower and turned to tones of apricot, coral, salmon, pink, and rose with hints of yellow at the fringes. I stopped on one photo, a beautiful tonal shot that captured the merging of many colors, and I stared long and hard, mesmerized at how the edges of one shade bled into the next. "That's life," I whispered as I realized how different parts of my life had bled into other areas, but that I was, at the end of the day, still me. I was a mix of all the colors that made up "me." That realization brought me a sense of peace that I didn't necessarily have to pick one or the other; instead, I might be able to find a way to blend what I wanted in my life.

I clicked to the next sunset shot. The frame silhouetted seagulls in front of the half-sunset, as if they'd been cued to take flight at precisely the right time to synchronize with the sun's position. I continued through the series of photos, one by one, and watched the sun disappear into the sea, just as Brooke and I had watched it on that evening. But as I sat behind my desk and watched it now, I was reminded of how short life is and that one day, I would see *my* final sunset. The next photo was of Brooke's laughing, smiling face as she looked into my lens. I wondered, as I stared at her, if she were meant to be with me, by my side for my last sunset. Or was it supposed to be Naomi, the strong, devout woman, the one who'd promised to honor her vows and stand by her man, through the good times and the bad, for richer or for poorer, in sickness and in health? The lump in my throat grew larger and I only felt more confused.

. . .

Brooke knew where things stood with Naomi, and she knew I was confused and overwrought. But she had no intention of lessening her grip or easing the consistent pressure she put on me. She'd set her sights on her goal and had latched on like a bulldog on a mission. But as I mentioned, Brooke always fancied herself the smartest person in the room—*any* room. This made her feel superior. But I was different. I'd always heard "If one finds himself the smartest person in a room, then he should find another room" to learn something new and broaden his horizons. Brooke did not subscribe to this notion, however. She enjoyed feeling like the one on top, the brightest, smartest, most sophisticated, most articulate, and so on.

Maybe it helped her compensate for her feelings of physical inadequacy; I never knew and never figured it out. I wasn't the therapist. All I knew was her snooty superiority was very unattractive, and it had nothing to do with her appearance.

Brooke's way of exerting pressure and forcing my hand was to make herself unavailable to me. She tried to use her version of reverse psychology to make me want what I couldn't have, as if I were a child. "No, sorry. I'm not free this afternoon," she'd say. "I've got plans." Or she'd take phone calls during our lunches or dinners together, as if those callers were more important than our time. Even when we talked about my marriage, Brooke casually tossed out comments like, "Maybe you ought to think about giving it another try," just to see my reaction and test the waters. But I knew what game she was playing, and frankly, it irritated me. Men are simple beings. We don't like games—except of the sexual kind. We require only a few things to keep us happy. But when life gets tangled and messy, we don't care for it. Brooke's game of pushing me away to make me want to get closer only pissed me off and made me begin to see her in a different light. When the games started, my perspective of her shifted, too. It was clear she was being steered by her friends and it was a "me against them" scenario. Little, by little, as Brooke's ugly side began to bubble to the surface, I felt a divide form between us.

CHAPTER 12

PRETTY WOMAN

One afternoon as I cleaned out my briefcase, I came across some old receipts. As I sorted through them, one caught my attention. It was from the upscale boutique where I'd taken Brooke shopping one day. I called it my "Pretty Woman Day" in reference to the Julia Roberts/Richard Gere movie in which the wealthy businessman takes the sassy hooker shopping at a high-end, classy dress shop. As I stared at the receipt, I remembered that day:

"I feel like a princess, just like royalty!" Brooke had gushed from inside the dressing room.

I had arrived at the posh boutique ahead of Brooke to speak with the saleswoman. She'd assisted me in pre-selecting some items for Brooke. She'd hung them in the dressing lounge and then prepared a champagne tray for us to enjoy when I returned with Brooke after I'd met her in the parking lot behind the boutique.

"Well, come out and model for me," I said, laughing as I sipped champagne and sat in an overstuffed Queen Anne chair that dwarfed even me, and I'm a big guy.

"Um, you'd better come here for this one, babe."

I knew she must be wearing the black silk bra and thong. So, I got up and was going over to the dressing room's twelve-foot tall door when she cracked it open. The saleswoman was in the room with her and had assisted her in trying on the lingerie.

"It's exquisite!" Brooke gushed. "I've never felt silk this nice, and the lace pattern is so intricate!"

"The lace is handmade in Le Puy, France," said the pretty saleswoman. "It's created by artisans using centuries-old looms. Each artisan's family has its own patterns and special techniques that are handed down."

"I've never owned anything so beautiful. It's too pretty to wear underneath clothing!" Brooke added.

My eyes devoured her shapely sexy body in that lingerie. I didn't think I had shared with Brooke the haunting lustful desires that welled in me when I saw such a stunning woman in lingerie. It put me into the primal mode of just wanting to take her right there— yes, lifting her on top of the sales counter and diving right in between her legs. I could imagine my face rubbing on the exquisite fabric between her juicy thighs and smelling the intoxicating sex pheromones I knew she was emanating. But my mind snapped back to reality as I just stood there in a primal gaze.

"Listen; I'd have to work for nearly a week to buy that bra," the saleswoman whispered to Brooke. "If I bought that, I'd be proudly parading it in public."

Both women agreed and broke out in laughter as the door closed. I went to my perch on the chair to wait and see the dresses I'd chosen for Brooke. Another saleswoman had already refilled my champagne glass, and she offered me a tray of hand-dipped chocolate strawberries tinged with edible 14-karat gold.

"I'm good, but thank you," I said, smiling.

"Incredible!" the saleswoman's voice said from inside the dressing room. "It fits like it was made for you! You must go out and show your husband!"

Seconds later, the door opened, and Brooke stepped out. The dress did look amazing on her. It was of excellent quality, and it fit her properly, disguising the negatives and accentuating the positives, like women prefer, and for the price, it should have done that and more. Just like a well-tailored suit makes the man, that dress made Brooke look better. She walked taller and looked happier than ever before. Her spirits were lifted, and she knew the quality dress in its subdued blue shade flattered her figure and her coloring.

"I can't believe how good you are at picking out clothes for me, Alex! I could have shopped all day and never come up with something half this awesome!"

"You look fantastic. The color, the fit, everything. I like it. Try on the other one—the black and silver one."

"Two for two!" Brooke said minutes later when the door opened and she came out in the second dress. "You've got great taste, Alexander—in dresses *and* in women."

When she disappeared back into the dressing room, I thought about her comment—and about Naomi, that cute girl in the gray coat I'd met so many years ago on my college campus. Yes, I did have great taste in women. So, what had led me to where I sat in that boutique, with my mistress trying on expensive designer dresses?

"Ready?" Brooke asked five minutes later when she came out, dressed in her own clothes again while the saleswoman carried the lingerie and the two dresses, all on satin-covered hangers.

"Shall I wrap and box everything?" the second saleswoman asked me, as she reached for the hangers from the first woman.

"Most definitely, please," I replied.

"Oh! Thank you, Alex! I feel like the luckiest girl! I've never owned things this nice, not ever! I can't wait to wear them!"

Brooke wrapped her arm through mine and stood on tiptoe to kiss me as I took my blue card from my wallet to pay for the mother lode being rung up at the marble sales counter. Again, men are simple beings. Give us a shirt and a pair of pants, and we're fine. But we do understand that women enjoy being pampered, and we understand that if women feel good, that will, in turn, make us feel good. So, not only would the boutique receive a windfall of good fortune on that day if all went as I'd planned.

As the perfectly coiffed woman at the register handed the expensive shopping bags to me with the beautifully wrapped clothing inside, I thanked her and said to Brooke, "Next stop, shoes."

"Really? Seriously? I *am* Julia Roberts!"

"No, you'd be *Vivian*, right?" I laughed. "She played *Vivian* in *Pretty Woman*, right?"

"Well, the jury's still out as to whether you're my Edward Lewis or my Richard Gere. Either way, *I* win!"

It was a fun afternoon. I'll admit I enjoyed taking Brooke out and exposing her to new things outside her ordinary life and beyond her means. She'd told me she appreciated the trips, the fine restaurants, the expensive wines, and all the decadent life experiences I'd shown her. Maybe I liked being her hero, the white knight who got to save the girl and take her out of her ordinary world. All I know is when I was with Brooke, I got to step out of my humdrum work-a-day monotony. It wasn't Brooke who was the allure. It wasn't that she was pretty or smart or funny or sexy or *anything* my wife was not. It wasn't that *she* was anything at all. It was the *circumstance* that was the allure, the respite, the break from reality. But while I was "in it," I couldn't see the truth of what I was doing, much less why I did it.

Brooke and I walked hand-in-hand through the quaint shopping village toward a high-end ladies' shoe store. It was a beautiful spring day with a light breeze, clear skies, and birds chirping in the treetops. Shoppers walked along the sidewalk and couples canoodled on benches while a few single people-watchers sat and enjoyed the weather.

"Did it bother you not to have a glass of champagne at the boutique?" I asked Brooke as I carried her shopping bags.

"Not at all. I'm happy to serve you, sir, and obey your wishes. Besides, I think the strict diet you recommended helped me to fit into those dresses."

"It helped me, years ago. But no matter what, I don't want you drinking wine or alcohol."

"As you wish, sir."

We turned to walk into the massive double doors of the upscale shoe store, and I held the door for Brooke. An hour later, I was laden with two additional shopping bags; I had purchased a couple of pairs of red-bottom Louboutin heels that had made Brooke moist with happiness the moment the salesman had slipped them onto her feet. As a guy who'd worn Herman Munster diabetic shoes much of his life, I had a hard time understanding all the hype and fuss behind those ultra-important women's shoes. Yet I planned to put them to good use, along with the fancy black lingerie I'd selected for Brooke. I fantasized how amazing her legs would look, propped open, hanging from the chains while wearing those shoes.

· · ·

I laughed at myself and tore up the insane receipts that had brought back memories of the shopping trip. What had I been thinking? Why had I thought Brooke had been deserving of such extravagance? But the more I pondered my questions, the more I began to form some semblance of an answer. Perhaps, I realized, men trade what they have in order to get sex, and women trade what they have in order to get love. It had all been a gigantic transaction, and I had used my currency to get what I'd felt I needed at the time. Brooke, on the other hand, had traded herself to get what she'd wanted: me and my lifestyle. We all leverage what we have to get what we desire. Some of us just happen to be better salesmen and closers than others. When I learned that using dominance worked for me, it became a part of my everyday toolbox, and I owned it as much as I owned every molecule of my makeup. Yet I still had that one, nagging question: *What do I do about my marriage?*

"You're clear on what I said, right?" Naomi asked one night. "If you get on that plane to Hawaii, we're done. I'm out. We're finished. You're not taking that bitch to Hawaii—or on the trip to Cabo, for that matter. To be clear, if you choose to take her on the trips with you, our marriage is done. You don't have to make the decision. I'll make it for you."

My daughter had been in my room earlier while I'd been packing. She thought I was going on a business trip since I hadn't told her otherwise. She looked sad and concerned, but when she'd walked out, Naomi came in to talk to me. She wasn't being unreasonable. She'd put up with a lot, a whole lot, more than almost any other woman would have tolerated. But I'd filed the divorce papers and taken that first step. We even had a court date and were supposed to go before a judge to be given our final divorce date. We were at the final stretch, and I was more confused than ever.

What did she want? What did Naomi want from me? Did she want me anymore? Did she want us? Had she only signed the divorce paperwork to make me wake up and get serious about what I'd been doing and what I'd be throwing away? Naomi just went on with refreshing my mind of our memories. Then it came out; she demanded that I not leave.

I refused to let Naomi tell me what to do. That's how I'd always been. I said goodbye to my family, grabbed my suitcase, and tossed it into my truck just before 6:30 a.m. As I drove to meet Brooke at her friend's house, where she'd arranged to leave her car while we were away, I phoned her and told her of Naomi's final ultimatum. She sounded worried.

"Should I stop driving?" Brooke somberly asked as she held her breath and waited for my answer.

I couldn't answer. I didn't know what to do or what I wanted. Finally, I told her to meet me as planned in thirty minutes at her friend's home where I'd pick her up. But after I hung up, I felt sick to my stomach and unsure whether I was doing the right thing. Naomi meant business. How could I destroy our family? I had no right.

"Hey, you made it!" Brooke said through her open car window when I pulled my truck next to her car in her friend's driveway. She looked happy to see me as she got out and reached for her suitcase to transfer it into my truck for the ride to the airport.

"Listen; leave that in your car," I told her. "You go ahead and drive to the airport. You should go on the trip. I can't go. Go on and go. I'll call you; it's fine. Hurry now, or you'll be late."

"What? Alex, no!"

"I'm not asking! Get in your car and drive to the damned airport, Brooke! Go!"

As I backed my truck from the driveway, Brooke stood in tears, still holding her suitcase. Her image got smaller and smaller in my rearview mirror as I forced myself to drive toward my home, toward the family Naomi and I had created. As I rounded the corner on our street, I saw her car was still in the driveway. I knew she'd still be getting ready for work. I walked inside with my suitcase in-hand and slowly walked toward my bedroom. From her bedroom, Naomi heard my heavy footsteps coming down the hallway.

"You didn't go, did you?" she called from her bedroom where she was still dressing.

"I sort of wanted to."

"Well, *go* then," Naomi said as she came to her doorway. She leaned against it to look at me as she put a gold hoop earring into her earlobe. "I mean it, Alex. If you *want* to go, then I want you to go. Don't stay here if you want to be somewhere else, not now, not ever."

I was so confused. With shaking hands, I pulled my cell phone from my pocket and hurried to call Brooke. Naomi went back to finish dressing so she wouldn't be late for work. As the phone rang against my ear, I retrieved my suitcase from my bedroom, retraced my steps, and ran back outside to my truck. My tires spun out on our street as Brooke answered her phone.

"I made a big mistake!" I breathlessly said. "I'm on my way to the airport now! I'll see you in a few minutes! Meet me at the gate!" Before Brooke could even reply, I hung up, ran a red light, and pressed down hard on the accelerator, intent on getting to the airport as quickly as possible.

Because of my diabetic condition, I had an airport Quick Pass that allowed me to use the medical security screening line at airports. With less people in that line, it always moved much faster.

By this time, I'd grown accustomed to my nerves being on edge, the residual result of my adulterous affair. Yet, while Naomi knew all about Brooke, our relatives and most of our friends still did not. After I'd checked my watch for the twentieth time, I nervously glanced around for familiar faces I might want to dodge since I was there to meet my mistress.

"You've got to be kidding me," I said aloud, but to no one at all, when I spied them as they walked nearer to my position in line.

"Pardon me?" the lady in front of me asked.

"Oh, uh, nothing. Sorry, ma'am."

What were the chances I'd run into Naomi's cousins at the airport? There was nowhere to run, no place to hide. I couldn't even step out of line without walking right past them since they were in the same enclosed security area. Since my line was shorter, it moved me closer, and snaked nearer to where Naomi's cousins stood with their carry-on luggage.

"Alex! Hey! How's it going?" Robert waved.

"Where's Naomi?" Cynthia asked as they came closer still.

"Hi, guys! Good to see you!" I lied. "Oh, Naomi's good. She's great, in fact, just great."

"And the kids?"

"Yep, kids are great, too, both of them."

"Where you headed?"

"Just headed on a quick business trip," I lied. I didn't want to say I was headed to Hawaii without my wife. That would have sounded odd, for sure, even *if* I was on a business trip. "What about you two? Where're you headed?"

"To see her college roommate's new baby."

"Nice. Well, safe travels. Good seeing both of you! We'll all have to get together soon."

"Definitely. Our love to Naomi and the kids!" Cynthia smiled as she and Robert walked farther away, thankfully.

When I made it through security, I made a beeline to Gate 87. To save time, I'd ignored Brooke's nonstop texts and calls that had been burning up my phone. I had already texted her when I'd parked at the airport parking garage. She knew I was making my way to her as fast as humanly possible.

Honestly, I'd expected a more exuberant welcome than the one she offered when I found her at Gate 87. After all, the woman had professed to loving me and called me her soulmate. I'd treated her extremely well, bought her jewelry, flowers, designer clothes, expensive dinners, and fine wines. I'd taken her along on luxury trips and shown her a nicer lifestyle than the one she'd known. She'd been exposed to a sophisticated world, different than her own before she'd met me. So, I had presumed that when she'd felt she might've lost me to Naomi and I'd gone home, she would have felt a sense of sadness and loss. Therefore, I'd thought she might feel relieved and happy to see me at the gate.

Yet my arrival was fairly anticlimactic. Brooke sat reading a celebrity gossip magazine, but she moved her carry-on bag from the chair beside her when I walked up so I could sit down. "You made it." She smiled as I exhaled deeply once I had finally fallen into the seat next to her, sweaty and heaving.

"I ran halfway through the concourse," I panted. "I thought you'd be boarding already."

"That's why I was trying to reach you. We're delayed about forty minutes. Can you watch my bags while I go grab a Starbucks espresso?"

CHAPTER 13

THE AWAKENING

Five hours later, our plane touched down on the tarmac at Kona International Airport. We had a few days of sun, fun, and unbridled sex in front of us. But something just didn't feel right. I looked around at all the people who stood with us, waiting to deplane, and I wondered about them. Was the young couple in Row 14 married? Were they happy? What about the old guy, two seats behind us? He wore a wedding ring but was traveling alone. Was he a widower? Did he live on the Big Island and was he coming home to his beloved wife of more than fifty years? How about the redheaded sexpot with the guy beside her who looked like a movie star? Were they a longtime couple traveling for a clandestine tryst to take some time for themselves and focus on each other? And how about the tall, leggy, hot blonde in Row 17, the one whose bust was busting out of her tank top? What was her story? Surely, she didn't have a significant other if she was still advertising the goods so prominently. I even wondered about the petite brunette in front of us. Was she arriving for a weekend romp in paradise before she tied the knot, and would she be forever off the market and stuck to one partner for all eternity?

"Do you think?" Brooke asked.

"What?"

"Have you heard a single thing I said to you, Alexander?" she scoffed, clearly irritated that I'd zoned out and missed whatever ultra-important statement she'd offered.

"Oh, never mind! Are you here, or not?"

I reached down, grabbed her wrist, and squeezed it as I stared down into her eyes. The pressure was just enough to remind her. No submissive should ever disrespect her Dom, and especially not in public. She looked up at me adoringly and her whole body relaxed. The passenger line began to move, and we made our way toward the front of the plane to the exit door.

"Thank you for flying with us. Enjoy your visit," the pretty Hawaiian flight attendant said as we passed her.

"Oh, we will; thank you." I winked at Brooke.

As we deplaned, we headed toward baggage claim and found an area of transportation drivers, all waiting with placards denoting various names. I walked toward the tall, muscular Hawaiian man in the floral shirt with the sign that had my name.

"Mr. Banks?" He smiled.

"I am." We shook hands and he said his name was Kai. I then introduced Brooke, by first name only, before our driver could presume her to be *Mrs.* Banks.

"Aloha!" Kai said as he draped a fresh flower lei around Brooke's neck.

"Thank you."

"And here is one for your hair, if you choose," he said as he handed her a pink plumeria bloom.

When Brooke began to put it behind her right ear, Kai said, "Did you know, ma'am, that in our culture, a lady wears a flower behind her left ear if she is taken and is in a serious relationship with a man?"

Brooke shot me a look that said she was both confused and irritated. To be honest, I was, too. Since she left the flower behind her right ear, I figured it was Brooke's way of letting me know she wasn't necessarily mine since I had wavered earlier in the day about whether to continue with the trip.

"Right this way, sir, madam," said Kai, still smiling. "I'll retrieve your bags and then I've got an Escalade waiting out front with some chilled Royal Mai Tai drinks in the back for you." He extended his arm so we could walk in front of him and toward the baggage area to point out our suitcases to him.

Minutes later, Brooke and I followed Kai as he carried our bags toward the resort's Escalade that he'd parked curbside. The moment we stepped outside the sliding doors, we were hit with the sweet perfumed scents only found in Hawaii, a mix of flora, fauna, and things still undiscovered but greatly appreciated by all who visit.

"Wow! It's a treat for the senses!" Brooke proclaimed as she inhaled deeply. "You've done it again, Alex! I can already tell I'm in for a treat!"

As we drove along Hawaii Highway 200 toward the resort, Brooke opened her window. She sat back against the leather seat and breathed in the blended scents of pineapple, plumeria, coconut, fresh rain, and a touch of eucalyptus. "This must be what heaven smells like," she said. But I didn't feel like I was in heaven, nor did I think I deserved to go there. I'd just officially left my wife of more than two decades and broken her heart, my son was more pissed off than ever, my daughter wasn't happy with me, and my feelings for Brooke weren't what they should have been for me to have upended my family's lives. What the hell had I done? I wasn't sure how to proceed or what to do next.

But, like any red-blooded American man, I did what I did best. I got to the resort, checked in to our suite, and then screwed Brooke for all I was worth since I knew she was expecting it from me, of course. Just after I'd drifted off to sleep, my phone rang. The screen said: *Naomi*. She knew I was with Brooke, so I felt something could have happened to one of the kids since she was calling me.

"Naomi? What happened? What's wrong?"

"I'll tell you what's wrong!" Naomi said, her voice slurred and garbled. "What you're doing is all wrong! But it's fine because I can go out and find a guy who'll be happy to have a wife like me, a good and decent woman!" She was drunk, half-crying, half-slurring her inebriated rant.

I got up and took my phone to the other room in our suite, away from Brooke. She even turned on the music in the bedroom to try to give me some privacy, but it didn't help enough. Naomi's wrath had built up over the months and she'd drowned her sorrows in alcohol, which had made things so much worse, and she was off on a wild rant, reminding me how much I had blown it, how I had personally destroyed my life by making the choices I'd been making.

"I have tried to be a good wife for you, Alex! What have I ever done to deserve what you've done to me, to us, to this family? You're such a selfish, damned…ugh!" She was so mad she hung up, unable to find the most expressive words to describe her fury at that moment. I immediately called her back, but she didn't pick up. Again, and again, I called her. Then my phone rang. It was my son. He was calling me to yell at me for upsetting his mom and breaking her heart.

"How can you do this to her? This isn't right!" he yelled. But he didn't want to hear anything I had to say either. He hung up on me, too. I tried to call him back, but he wouldn't take my calls either. Again, I dialed Naomi. Same thing, no answer. No one would speak to me. Everyone was furious with me.

As I sat with my head in my hands and my elbows resting on my knees, Brooke walked into the front room of our suite. She wore a God-awful, frumpy-looking white baby doll nightie. This monstrosity of tacky, white fabric made her look totally thick and unattractive. Showing off her thickness, bumps, and lumps, the white fabric got lost against her pale white skin. I looked down at my phone and then back at my now pissed-off lover, an ill-timed disaster before me. So off to bed I went. Crawling into bed with what I now called "the ice queen," I tried everything to warm that emotionally cold exterior and get a bit frisky. Vanilla sex it was since all my kinkiness got railroaded by her attitude. After about an hour of one-sided pleasure, looking at her resting bitch face made me just get more frustrated and throw in the towel regarding any kind of satisfying sex. Brooke now shared that she hadn't wanted to have sex with me, and the only reason we had even tried was that she'd felt obligated since I'd brought her along on the trip. "Fantastic," I said. "I've been reduced to quid pro quo. This only gets better. I'm going to sleep now." Upon rolling over, she muttered under her breath, just enough for me to hear, "That was the worst sex ever." Her words cut deeply, not only into my manhood but also into the dominant man I had tried so hard to become. Everything I believed about myself came crashing down.

As I lay on my pillow in the dark, with the ice queen beside me, I thought, "Great. I've just ruined my family for *this*."

In the morning, after a fitful night's sleep, if it could even be called that, I showered and then joined Brooke downstairs in the resort's dining room for breakfast. The writing was on the wall. I knew it. I felt it. After the young Hawaiian girl had brought my water with fresh pineapple garnish in it, I looked across at Brooke, and then I leaned in to speak to her.

"You're going to leave me, aren't you?"

"I was going to wait until after the trip," she admitted.

"Why wait?" I slammed my chair back, stood up, and started to walk out of the restaurant. Halfway out, I stopped in my tracks. I immediately went back to the table, lifted Brooke up by the hand, gave her the most passionate kiss right there in front of everyone in the room, and then whispered in her ear.

"I will always love you. You have a piece of my heart I can never get back; please take care of it and hold it precious." Then, in haste, I was out of the room and went up to the bedroom to pack and get the hell out of Dodge. In less than ten minutes, I threw my clothes and belongings into my suitcase and then headed to the concierge desk to hail a cab to the airport. I'd lost two women in only twelve hours. It must have been some sort of record, I was sure. I felt like I'd be better off dead and my family would be so much better off without me. I had royally screwed up everything and allowed myself to be played by Brooke.

No father wants to be a failure in his kids' eyes, but I couldn't imagine how I'd ever come back from the mess I'd made of our lives. I'd really dropped the ball as far as my son and daughter were concerned, and worst of all, I had hurt their mother, a virtually unforgivable offense. How in hell could I be a dominant man when I had callously trampled the woman who'd always stood by me, praised me when I was down, and built our family's lives? How could I expect to be the dominant one when it was Naomi who had steadfastly hung on with the strength of an army while she felt eviscerated by the one person whose trust should have never been in question? My kids and my wife may have hated me, but I despised myself far more. I felt ashamed of the man in the mirror, and it seemed there would never be a way out of the disaster I'd created.

Depressed and guilt-ridden, I spent hours curled in the fetal position, sobbing uncontrollably and wailing in emotional pain. It wasn't just pain from what I'd done. It came from decades earlier, even from my childhood. The pain had been buried for so long, hidden away and blocked out, so that I'd never have to face it and it could never again touch or hurt me. There were unresolved issues, long-forgotten angsts, twisted pangs from my past, childhood embarrassments, and petty judgments. They all bubbled to the surface and simultaneously exploded in a violent cataclysmic revolt too powerful to be contained.

A couple of days later, my tormented soul wailed like a wounded animal as my curled form wracked and shook uncontrollably. I could take no more. I picked up my .45-caliber revolver to stop all the pain, once and for all. With the cold metal barrel in my mouth, I cocked the gun and then shut my eyes. I thought of my kids and of Naomi. I hoped they'd forgive me and that they knew how much I loved them. I took a deep breath and held it, and then with a trembling hand, I began to move my index finger toward my palm. But suddenly, my brother's voice came into my head and I froze. I heard his voice remind me of what he'd said several times before: "Never make a long-term decision to solve a short-term problem."

"Shit!" I cried aloud as I pulled the gun from my mouth. He was right. My problem seemed monumental in the moment, but it would pass. I'd get through it. But I had to hang on and fight to fix the mess I'd made of everything. Leaving my family wasn't the answer.

But I was in anguished pain, actual physical pain that I felt deep in my gut. In half a day, I had lost two women, two very important women. I truly felt uncertain how to go on for another day. When I looked at my watch, I realized I didn't have to worry about tomorrow or even the next hour. I only had to focus on the next few minutes. So that's what I did. I fought through the pain and overwhelming sadness and loneliness, and I did it a few minutes at a time.

"Five more minutes," I reminded myself. "Just five. You've got it, man. Just five." The first hour was the hardest and the longest, for sure. In fact, it was the longest hour of my life. Those sixty minutes found me caught somewhere between life and death as I straddled my own mortality and fought the urge to stop breathing, just to end the searing pain. But after the first hour had passed, I marked a small victory, albeit a silent one. After that, I made myself get through the next hour and then the next two, and then the next morning, and then the next day, and so on.

Naomi saw my struggle. I was at home and cloistered away in my bedroom. I wanted to see no one and to talk to no one. Even I had no clue how my mental crash would end. Naomi looked worried for me, and I felt ashamed that I'd added to her burden. She brought me food, but I never ate it. She tried to sit with me, but I didn't want the company. She tried to talk to me, but I had no energy for conversation. I kept my door shut so my daughter wouldn't have to watch her dad's mental decline. I'd put her and my son through too much already.

"What is it that you really want, Alex?" Naomi asked one night as she lay beside me on my bed in my dimly lit room. I didn't answer her. She got up and walked to the bedroom door, stopped, and turned back toward me.

"If you truly love her, then just go and get her. Send her some flowers," she suggested before she went to her own bedroom.

Naomi's suggestion stupefied me to my core. It had been entirely unselfish and straight from her heart. She'd watched my suffering for over a week; she'd seen how badly I was hurting—how raw and guttural was my pain. After two decades of marriage, Naomi loved me enough to let me go if it meant I would be happy and my pain would stop. She was willing to hurt herself and go through her own pain and loss for me to stop hurting, even if it meant losing me to Brooke. In all my years, I'd never known anyone so unselfish. It was difficult to digest what I'd just heard.

Grappling for guidance, I even had a psychic reading to get some direction before I approached Brooke. I couldn't afford to screw it up with her, not after all I'd already suffered. Brooke and I were such opposites. In the past, when I'd bought her flowers, she'd said, "Oh, don't buy me flowers." She said it, though, with a bit of disdain in her voice, like it was a waste. I could never figure out which was the waste—the money I spent on flowers or that I had taken the time to pick out what I thought would be the perfect flowers to bring a smile to her face. She had just made my effort look simple and ridiculous. Just a traditional male copout gesture. Thinking about our personal differences even more, I reflected on how I had always been a guy who enjoyed all types of music, and I considered myself to have eclectic tastes. Yet Brooke was a devout heavy metal rocker chick. She refused to consider any bands that didn't sound like or resemble groups like AC/DC, Black Sabbath, Iron Maiden, Slayer, or Korn. "How do you listen to that stuff?" I once asked her. She said the lyrics comforted her, especially during difficult times, but I had joked, "*What* lyrics?"

The psychic had suggested I send Brooke flowers, saying they had to be special ones. "She will know the meaning behind the flowers," Alicia Killabrew explained. "Choose carefully and send the precise message you wish to convey to this woman."

Before I called the florist shop, I talked with Naomi again, just to make sure she'd be okay with it if I tried to get Brooke back. "Look, Alex; do what makes you happy. I want you happy, not dead." I couldn't believe my good fortune to have found such a woman, a person who genuinely cared about me and my personal happiness. Even as a boy, I hadn't had that gift. But by now, Naomi and I were living as platonic roommates, simply fuck buddy friends once in a while, who shared and loved the same children. Still, for the first time in my entire life, someone had put my happiness first, even at the expense of their own. I was awed by Naomi's overwhelming generosity and the gift she'd given me. A gigantic weight lifted from my shoulders and from my heart, thanks to Naomi, and an age-old wound had healed deep inside of me. At that moment, we might not have had a passionate, romantic love, but I definitely loved Naomi.

· · ·

"Hello? Yeah, I'd like to know if you've got fresh orchids in stock," I asked the florist on the phone. She asked me to hold while she checked on the orchids. "Yes, we do have some. We can make you an arrangement with the fresh orchids and we can deliver it for you today, if you'd like," the woman confirmed.

I hoped the psychic had been right that Brooke knew her flowers. I'd had to look up the meanings of various blooms to figure out the message I wanted to send her. Who knew a simple flower sent cryptic messages and had hidden meanings? I'd always looked at an orchid and seen just an orchid. But not anymore.

Brooke didn't call me right away. She made me sweat just a little bit longer, even after I received confirmation from the florist that she'd received the floral arrangement I had sent to her. But finally, a day later, she called. When I saw her name on my phone's screen, my heart leapt. My pulse quickened, and with a sweaty, shaking hand, I answered.

"Hi, Brooke." I closed my eyes and heard my heart pounding in my head.

"Alexander. Hi. How are you?"

"Pretty good. How are you?"

"Good. I wanted to thank you for the flowers."

I waited, hesitant and uncertain whether she knew the message behind the stems I'd chosen for her.

"I'm looking at them right now, actually," she went on. "It's so like you to do something so classy and sophisticated, Alexander. As soon as I saw them, I knew what they meant."

Finally, I exhaled. "Good. I was hoping you'd understand."

"It's perfectly romantic. Of course, I know orchids mean you are *declaring your love for only me*, and *you prefer me above all others*."

I thought I heard her sniffling as if she might be crying. I hoped it was a good sign. "Can we get together and talk?" I asked. "I want to tell you that myself, in person."

"Why don't you come by tonight?"

• • •

Brooke and I got back together, and at first, I thought I was right where I was meant to be. Naomi and I continued to live in our family home and our kids went on to their respective lives. Brooke and I returned often to the dungeon club for our sex play, and we had as much sex as we could fit into our waking hours.

"Hey, buddy!" a friend said in a phone message one day. "Let's go get those new tattoos we've been talking about. How's Saturday? Call me!"

As it turned out, my friend didn't make it to meet me at the tattoo parlor, but I got my own tattoo anyway. I'd had some previous ink art done, and I always chose designs that had special meaning to me. This time was no different.

"What do you think?" the tattoo artist asked as he pushed his stool back and turned the light so I could see his artwork on my skin.

"I'm exactly where I want to be" was on my left forearm, my reminder that in life, there are no accidents and God doesn't make mistakes. Those six little words would empower me, remind me, lift me up, and save me many times over the next three months. That was my reason for placing the tattoo in an easily accessible and visible location.

Although we'd gotten back together, my relationship with Brooke was far from perfect. She still worked harder at playing games and psychoanalyzing me than she did at improving our relationship. One evening, I was at her house watching TV when her son came in.

"Hey, Mom, are you going to the Watsons' Halloween party?" he asked Brooke.

"Yeah, I am," she confirmed.

"What party is that?" I asked. "Are you talking about Dave and Amanda?"

"Oh, um, well, yes, but you weren't invited. Is that a problem?" Brooke stammered. "Oh, listen; I can just change my plans and we can do something else. No big deal."

"No," I replied. "I think you should go to the party. That was your plan, obviously. Go ahead and go."

We had been to Dave and Amanda's home a couple of times before for get-togethers. I actually loved to spend time with them and some of Brooke's other friends. We had played games and just hung out. I knew from the whole tone of the conversation that Brooke had come home from the trip that I left her on and totally blasted me to them. She was the persecuted one. I am sure in her story she was totally the victim. I am sure nothing was mentioned about the wonderful time we had shared, or the absolutely blissful times when we just got lost in one another's eyes.

In the end, Brooke asked me to accompany her to the party although I didn't feel especially welcomed by anyone there, not the hosts nor the guests. "Wow, they were pretty cold and standoffish toward me tonight," I said when we got back to Brooke's house.

"Well, you did leave me in Hawaii," she replied.

"I can think of worse places to be left. The trip was paid for, and besides, you were going to break it off with me! Did you mention that to your judgmental cronies, those snooty bitches who glared at me down their noses and whispered behind my back all night?"

I didn't care for some of her friends, and Brooke seemed like she wanted to keep some of them from me. Her girlfriends had banded together with her, just like before, when we'd been broken up. I could tell they were chirping in her ear. It felt like they were constantly plotting and conspiring, and as if they didn't care for me at all. I presumed that was why Brooke kept me from them. It was like we had our fun and our life, but Brooke had another separate life she didn't want to include me in. It didn't feel good that I'd been aching over and pining for a woman who didn't even want to invite me into her inner circle. It didn't make me feel good that I'd bought her multiple pairs of red-bottomed Christian Louboutin heels and that she walked all over me in them, behind my back. Once again, it soon became clear that Brooke felt obliged to trade pumps for *pumps*. In her mind, if we each got something we wanted, we should both be satiated. She had a select amount of very nice dresses and accessories in her closet that I had given her. Better than what she had ever thought of buying for herself. I am sure that in her mind, she'd given me something in return: my every sexual desire and fantasy fulfilled.

"Damn!" my brother exclaimed when I brought him up to speed one day. "Man, I think that's called prostitution."

"Funny you should mention that. Did I tell you about one of her first jobs?"

"Well, looks like she's still moonlighting, huh?" he replied.

I didn't want to hear it, from him or anyone. I just wanted to ignore the opinions and have my life the way I dreamed it to be.

CHAPTER 14

REVELATIONS

I decided to take things a bit slower with Brooke. After the party and feeling unwanted, I decided just not to make myself as "available" to her in my schedule. I decided to really think about me and what I wanted in my life. I gained a new perspective on our overall relationship. When I reflected on our time together, I was reminded of another personal situation that had seemed to be one way and was really an entirely different reality. Years earlier, one of my brothers had asked my other brothers and me to buy him out of the business; then he'd left with his payout from the business. At first, we'd thought he had been a huge *asset* and we would surely miss all his support within the business. But we quickly found he'd been nothing more than a huge *ass*. When he left, we all breathed a sigh of relief and things actually got better. It was the same with Brooke. I'd never known how much she'd held me back, stalled my pace, and thwarted my life's progress until I was free of her for a while.

Random things continued to conjure up memories of time spent with Brooke. For instance, ongoing situations arose with my health. Once, after Brooke and I broke up, a doctor prescribed a TENS (transcutaneous electrical nerve stimulation) unit to help manage my neuropathic pain.

"This unit sends tiny electrical pulses through the skin. It works to stimulate endorphins and other substances that act as your body's natural pain killers. Some patients report a pleasant, almost euphoric sensation, at times. The nurse will show you how to set up the unit and properly position the pads for optimum results," the doctor explained.

Little did the neurologist know I'd had plenty of experience with a TENS unit—during sex play. The first time I had used the battery-operated device with Brooke, I'd wanted to ensure she knew my feelings about a flippant, somewhat mocking threat she'd made one day. We had been talking about how I'd cheated on Naomi and how she might have felt about the infidelity.

"Well, if you ever cheated on me," Brooke laughed in a threatening tone, "I'd just go online and find someone to cheat with, too. Simple as that!"

I thought about this attempt at intimidation and decided to nip her snarky attitude in the bud. She needed to know just where I stood on her tossing loose-lipped threats. She was fairly brazen to have lobbed the casual comment in the first place, but by this point, I knew how much Brooke enjoyed being on the precipice between pain and pleasure, dangling on the edge and toying with danger. It was no secret to either of us that such precious scenarios made her juices flow like nothing else.

So, after a day of reflecting on Brooke's threat to go out and have sex with other men, I decided to remind her of the only man in her life—the only one she needed. After a quick stop at a medical supply store, I continued on the drive to her home, late in the afternoon following a meeting with our company CPA. The whole time our resident bean-counter had been pontificating about the straight-line depreciation method he preferred, my mind had drifted off to how I'd use my new sixty-dollar gadget to make clear my expectations to Brooke.

"Ron, if you'll just finish all the returns, I'll sign them and then get them back to you," I finally interrupted. "I've got another meeting outside the office. I need to take off."

As our stone-faced accountant pushed his wire-rimmed glasses back onto the bridge of his nose, he looked dejected and sad. He reminded me of how as a boy I'd felt I didn't fit in with the other kids. Ron always lit up when he talked about figures, expenses, tax codes, and those boring things that put most people to sleep. Accounting was his life's passion, and it dominated his world. But my mind was on another passion, and my dominance did not have a thing to do with crunching numbers.

"But, Alex, but…" Ron called behind me as I walked from my office. "We didn't get to the estimated useful life of the offices and the warehouse. And what about the new equipment I need to ask you about?"

"Take care of it, Ron. The best managers know how to hire good people and then let them do their jobs! I've done my job; now do yours, Ron."

As I drove toward Brooke's house, I purposely did not call her or send her a text. I wanted my arrival time to be a surprise. When I put my key in her lock, I was over an hour early. Her old dog loved me, so he only lazily opened one eye as he lay on his bed near the foyer. As he drifted back to sleep to finish his pre-dinner nap, I quietly walked inside to surprise her. Since music played from her bedroom, I presumed she was in her room either resting or getting ready for my arrival, since she'd likely gotten home from work an hour earlier. The bedroom door was open, and my feet were almost silent on her thick hallway carpeting. I walked closer as old-school rock played from the Bose sound system. I never could understand how she found that crap relaxing, but it was all she seemed to enjoy.

"Back in Black" by AC/DC filled the room. I stepped to the doorway and looked inside. The song continued as she lay still, eyes shut, and wrapped in a towel, atop her eggplant-colored satin comforter on her bed. I paused to consider which of my several options I'd use. I had thought of a few. I needed to make my point. I would not be misunderstood. I would be very clear, and I would punctuate my statement with no ambiguity so there would be no question what I'd meant. I walked closer, then stopped beside her, and looked down at her totally relaxed, entirely vulnerable form. I was furious, filled with rage that she'd dared to threaten me with her childish comment. As her taunting voice echoed in my ears, I drew back my hand.

THWACK!

Her body came off the bed as she grabbed her bottom and then rolled away from the sudden searing pain. Before she could speak, I smacked her other ass cheek with the same intensity, just for good measure. "Don't you ever threaten me again! You will *not* date another man! That is not an option while you are with me. You can serve only one master. Am I clear?" My hand stung like pins and needles from the firm spanking, but it felt oddly good.

Her eyes were wide, but not with fear. Brooke's gaze was wild with excitement. I bent down and grabbed a handful of her brunette hair, then twisted it hard at her scalp. As I pulled her toward me, her floral lilac towel fell off and she was entirely nude. But she didn't look frightened as much as she appeared turned on and ready for play. Her erect nipples were at attention and begging for just what I'd had in mind.

"You're early, sir!" she gasped.

"You are never to threaten me that you will see another man!" I repeated. "Am I clear? I never want to hear those words come from your mouth, not ever! Or else, I will be gone, for good!"

"I only wanted to let you know how I felt," she said. "I wanted for you to be jealous. I only want you, sir."

"Don't play games with me!"

I dropped her back onto the bed and took the TENS unit from my pocket. When she saw it, her eyes lit up, but I ignored her as I went about my work. I ordered her to lie back as I placed the electrodes on her pink nipples. She didn't protest; she was eager, in fact, to take whatever punishment I had to offer. I pulled the leather hand restraints and the new leather-padded mouth ball gag from her nightstand and bound her wrists above her head, then placed the gag in her mouth, as her breathing quickened and her breasts heaved in anticipation. As Brooke watched, I went to close the bedroom door so as not to disturb her old dog—I'm not a barbarian. When I turned toward her, she playfully struggled and contoured her body as if she were taken against her will. I made her watch me as I peeled off my shirt and then studied her.

I slid my hand up her inner thigh until I could feel her moistness radiate from her groin. She was soaked and ready to be ridden hard. But I'd make her wait. I sat down in the chair beside her bed and checked my email on my phone. I even paid a couple of bills from my phone, just to heighten her impatience. She had to know who was in control. She must be taught a memorable lesson.

Fifteen minutes later, I stood over her and picked up the small black control device. She looked excited but also a bit frightened. "If you are with me, then you are mine, only *mine*!" I accentuated my last word by dialing the TENS control to an intensity that made her shriek a muffled, garbled squeal from behind the black leather gag as her body arched off the bed. I watched her breasts as they pulsated on and off with different degrees of intensity. Brooke's eyes were wide with fright but also excitement. I knew she was torn between wanting me to stop and wanting more of the same. My insatiable little minx had the most peculiar appetite. I had to admit that I liked it.

"If you want to be with me, then you will be only with *me*!" I repeated, again turning the dial on the TENS. "Don't you ever make those threats to me again, woman! No one threatens me, not ever, and especially not with another man! Am I clear?"

Her body jerked and twitched, and tears ran down her cheeks, but she couldn't answer. "Now, if I remove the gag, don't scream," I said. "Otto was sleeping in the foyer when I came in." She nodded in agreement, as always wanting to put her beloved Great Pyrenees before her own needs, as I'd known she would. "I'll ask you again," I said as I took the leather gag from her drooling mouth, "am I clear that *no one* ever threatens me, especially with another man?"

"Yes, sir, quite clear."

Sweat glistened on her skin and her eyes were wild with desire as she looked up at me. We both knew Brooke wanted me to leave the now taunt leather cuffs on her wrists and attached above her head. It was difficult to know which of us preferred her vulnerability more as darkness lazily blanketed the scene. The room smelled of amber and patchouli, compliments of the lit candle on the nightstand beside the bed as Black Sabbath pumped out the lyrics from their classic "Iron Man." As I looked down at Brooke, I got an idea. When I reached for the large glass candle jar, her eyes flashed with excitement and her nipples became erect, eager for what would come next.

Ever so slowly, I tilted the glass vessel as I held it above her chest. She bowed her back and lifted her breasts to meet the delicious hot wax. When the soy wax dribbled and splattered onto her chest and ran down her breast, Brooke winced just a bit. But almost simultaneously, she moaned in pleasure as the wax quickly dried on her skin. I repeated the process once, twice, three more times. Her eyes rolled back in her head. Brooke bit her lower lip in exquisite contentment. It was clear to both of us that I had reminded her of just why I was her one and only sir, the singular person who could deliver the pleasure she craved and coveted.

"Do you think I will need to teach you this lesson again?"

"*Need* to? There will be no *need*, sir."

We both knew I'd made my point. While I had my willing submissive right where I wanted her, I removed the rest of my clothes. I stood beside the bed and put my cock in her mouth. I let her work it for a few minutes as the reflection from the candlelight bathed Brooke's face; then I dipped my own wick into her warm, flowing juices. I released her handcuffs afterward, when I was sure there was no question about her ownership and no gray area as to whom she belonged.

As always, conversation with Brooke turned to my marriage. She always pried and questioned me as to what had gone on with Naomi since the last time we'd spoken about it. I knew what she was doing, even though Brooke tried so hard to use her therapist techniques to disguise her speculative prying.

"How's Naomi's overall attitude been?" But before I could even answer her, Brooke was on to the next question. "What does it seem like she's thinking? Can you tell what she wants to do? Is she still sleeping in the master bedroom and are you in the other—"

"Which question do you want me to answer, woman?" I interjected, just to stop the rapid-fire barrage.

"Alex, I'm just trying to make conversation and find out how you've been doing; that's all."

Brooke lobbed her repetitive open-ended questions, the irritating kinds of questions men hate because they invite conversation that can span into infinity. I just wanted to make the prolonged inquisition stop! The gag was always my friend. I replaced it over her mouth, and then I had her again. Reaching under the bed, I grabbed a couple of my acrylic canes. I stood next to the bed and proceeded to gently drum her rounded ass like a drum set. Beating to the music in what I call "rhythmic caning," she melted into the mattress and began to board that shuttlecraft in her head on that trip to subspace. For an hour, I tantalized her behind with rhythmic whacks, some gentle, some firm, and when the music allowed, some very firm welt-raising beauty marks. When I'd finished, I went to shower while Brooke went to cook me a traditional five-course Italian dinner, from antipasto to dolce.

• • •

I had it good at the time, or at least, I had what I thought was a good setup. I got to go visit Brooke and do whatever I pleased. During our clandestine rendezvous, I took a mini-vacation from reality—a pleasant retreat from all the stresses and discomforts that go with it. Gone were all the pressures, all the weighty worries, and all the forces that seemed to work against me. When I was with Brooke, there were no troubles, no responsibilities, no bills to pay, no deadlines nor expectations, and no old baggage from the previous arguments and prior disappointments that accompany all long-term relationships. When I was with Brooke, life wasn't real, but it took some time for me to realize the truth. Sure, the mood was relaxed and easy with Brooke, and there was always the thrill of the expectation of great sex and some delicious caning and flogging that I knew always awaited. But when I was with her, much was also lacking. There was no connection to the one and only special woman who'd stood by me all of my adult years, being my champion and helping me through the worst of times. With Brooke, there was no cute girl who'd caught my eye and given me butterflies in my stomach for the first time. With her, there was no remembrance of the first woman I'd stolen a kiss from and then nervously awaited for a reaction from in hopes she felt as I had. There wasn't the first time I took Naomi's virginity and kept it all for my own. With Brooke, there weren't shared memories of our kids' first steps, their first words, and all those milestones that forever cement new parents and become the foundation for families. But while I was with Brooke, I was too close to have a good perspective of what was happening. Sure, I thought my situation was fantastic, that kind of arrangement most guys only dream about living. Yet while I was immersed in my pseudo-simpatico lifestyle, the calendar pages continued to flip and time marched on. Naomi had been more than patient with me, too, while she'd allowed me to explore all the supposed freedoms I'd missed out on in my earlier days. Even after the divorce papers had been filed, Naomi had continued to be civil toward me and we'd agreed that we'd remain on good terms. We still had one final step in the divorce proceedings. We were to appear before a judge to get that final stamp of approval that would, in fact, declare our intention to formally divorce. The date was coming up. We both knew the date was drawing nearer; although we did not discuss the divorce per se, we did talk about other things.

At one point, we'd even talked about how we still had love for one another. Those conversations left me more than confused, I'll admit. It was after those conversations that I drew strength from the specially designed tattoos that stared back at me from the mirror. In the last couple of years, I had always turned to tattoo ink to express myself, to commemorate important times in my life, or to empower myself. It was my way of memorializing how I'd been feeling. I'd even once taken my daughter along to get her a tattoo, but at the last minute, she'd changed her mind. That was fine with me. By that time, I'd grown used to the woman's prerogative to change her mind. But I told her if she wasn't 100 percent sure she wanted a tattoo, she should wait.

For me, tattoos have always been a reinforcement or a remembrance. The designs I've chosen either reinforce how I feel about someone or something, or else they're to remember or commemorate a special time in my life. Each one has a story attached to it and a deep meaning. Still today, when I look at my winged gladiator tattoo, any doubts leave me and I get an infusion of strength, my reminder that I can do anything. I've looked at that inked design many times and drawn strength that's propelled me and carried me through some tough times. I've also got other designs that have been created for me to commemorate healthy hurdles I've surmounted and overcome. If every picture tells a story, then I'm a walking rendition of *War and Peace*, and you'd better sit down because it'll take a while to hear all the details of my whole story!

Some people simply arrive at a tattoo parlor with no clue about what design they want the artist to create for them. Most of those people end up getting some uninspired, bland, meaningless nothing they very likely come to regret. Others haphazardly get inked during an impromptu drunken stupor. My tattoos have much more sentiment behind them. Each one has a purpose, even today. The tattoos I have with chains and bound women who seek and look to me for protection, shelter, and absolute love have special meaning to me, partly because of how much I enjoy the chains in our roleplay games, and partly because I know, in my earlier years, I was bound by invisible chains, actually a dominant man restrained and held back from being who he was meant to be in this world. Throughout my life, I always felt bound by obligations to parents or business, kindly putting others' priorities before my own, and bound by my own fear of stepping out from the norm of other people's judgments. Maybe that's why I like chains so much today—because I'm on the other side of them, and not wearing them, myself.

CHAPTER 15

THE LITTLE VOICE

The day came when it was time for Naomi and me to report to the courthouse and finalize our divorce date with a judge. It was supposed to be quick, just get a date of the final hearing, work out the details before then, and we would be done. Nothing felt right about the day, not from the moment I opened my eyes. I'd been dreading the day. It was a do or die, no turning back moment, and for a guy who'd been riding the fence for as long as I had, I didn't like being in that predicament. Before I even got out of bed, I tried to come up with the right answer. Once again, my brain desperately attempted to make order out of chaos as I considered all the questions that had pummeled me for so long: Do I really want a divorce? Is this what I want to do to my family? Will this solve all my problems? Why is it so hard to make this damned decision?

"Alex? Coffee's ready," Naomi called from the hall. "We need to be down there in about an hour-and-a-half."

"Yeah, thanks."

Did I want to live the rest of my life without Naomi in it? Was that the answer? Would I regret doing this?

I showered and dressed, but I still had no more clarity than before I'd gotten out of bed. When I went into the kitchen, I found Naomi at her laptop with a cup of coffee. She was dressed and ready to go. Something about her flippant demeanor, how casually she behaved, and her bizarre calmness, made me especially uneasy. Was I the only one in our duo who felt mournful that we were about to dissolve our marital bond forever? Had Naomi already emotionally moved on? Had I driven her away with my behavior? She'd been patient for so long. It had been an unusual reaction for a wife to allow a husband his dalliances, and it had been ultra-crazy that Naomi had even helped me get ready to go out on some of my dates. Some of my buddies had joked with me about it even. "Yeah, I'd check the brakes on your truck, man." "Sure, she's being nice. She's tripled your life insurance!" "Don't eat anything she cooks for you!" "No woman is that calm in this situation. What's the going rate for a hitman?"

But Naomi had waited me out. She'd told me she loved me and she wanted me to get it all out of my system and then come back to her. Yet as the court date had approached, everything still seemed uncertain. I'd expected to have a huge epiphany, some giant light-bulb moment that would tell me what to do. But it didn't come.

"We should get going," Naomi said. "We can each drive our own cars, or we can drive down to the courthouse together; your choice."

Suddenly, I realized it might be the last time I'd ride in the car with my wife. It would be the final drive with my wife, the mother of my children. There would never be another drive when we'd be married, husband and wife. The finality of it all hit me full force, like a Category Five hurricane.

"So?" Naomi asked. "What do you want to do?"

"Oh, uh—I guess—yeah, I guess we can drive together."

We barely spoke as we drove to the courthouse, each lost in our thoughts. I wondered if the kids knew their parents were about to be unmarried, divorced, uncoupled very soon from now. Did they know Naomi and I were about to royally screw up their lives in less than hour? Did they know we were just one step closer to getting a final divorce date? All of the things families go through with divorced parents. Whose house will Christmas be at? How do we handle holidays? My God, my mind just kept spinning thinking about all of the havoc.

When we walked into the courthouse, my legs felt leaden, as if I could barely move one in front of the other. We went through the metal detector and then found we were to go to Courtroom 12D at the end of the East Wing. Since it took so long to get through the security checkpoint, with everyone emptying their pockets and being hand-checked with a wand, we had to hurry to make our appointed time before the judge. "Come on!" Naomi urged. "What is it?" My legs weren't cooperating as I tried to walk down the long corridor. It felt like everyone around me was moving in slow-motion, as if in a cartoon. I couldn't force myself to go faster. It was like some invisible force was in front of me and pushing against me, almost like I was walking against a strong wind. Naomi was looking at me as if something was wrong with me, as I pushed my legs down the hall.

After what had seemed like a ridiculously long time, I finally got to the last door. My chest ached, my throat closed up, and my mouth went dry all at once. We walked into the courtroom and took our seats as sweat poured down my face. I looked over at Naomi, the only woman I'd ever loved, as she sat beside me. What the hell was I doing? I reached for her hand and held it. She looked surprised but didn't pull away.

"Do you want to do this?" I asked.

"Oh, no. What do you want, Alex? This is all you."

"I don't fucking know."

"Well, we are here so…."

She looked afraid to hear my answer, hesitant to believe it. I knew it was because she wanted to avoid being hurt again.

"I'm sure, yeah. I don't want a divorce."

Now, she looked relieved. I kissed her. Her eyes filled with tears and a look of relief as the worry lines seemed to relax in her face.

"Come on." I took her hand, pulled her up, and we walked up to the clerk in the front of the courtroom. The judge hadn't yet walked in.

"Ma'am, excuse me? What happens if we just didn't show up today?"

She glanced at the paperwork in my hand and recognized it immediately.

"Nothing; you just don't have the divorce granted; that's all. You'd still be married. It's like the proceeding never happened, and you don't get your $382 filing fee back. It will just be dismissed."

I proceeded to look at the clerk and said with a choked-up, tear-fighting lump in my throat, "Well then, would you just put down that we did not show up, please?" Naomi and I both grinned and rushed out, hand in hand. My legs worked fine now as we nearly ran out of the courthouse. When we got outside, Naomi stopped and said, "Alex, are you sure?"

"Yes, I promise. I am," I told her.

"And what about Brooke?" she asked.

"I've been done with her; it's over. In fact, I'll show you, once and for all. It's done."

I took out my phone and called Brooke from the courthouse steps as Naomi watched.

"Remember how you once said I should give my marriage another shot?" I asked Brooke as soon as she answered. "I'm doing it."

"Well," Brooke replied, "is there anything you want to say to me before you never get to speak to me again? Because when we hang up, I'm wiping you out of my life for good!"

I'll admit I felt nervous, but I said, "Just always know, I love you; you have a piece of my heart I can never reclaim," and then, I hung up the phone. Naomi looked happy for the first time in a long time.

I heard later from a mutual friend that Brooke wiped me from existence in her phone and from her social media contacts. She took everything out of her home that reminded her of me and sent my belongings back to me, pictures of us and all. She did seem to keep all of the nice gifts I had given her, though; I guess they were the consolation prize. There had been a time when I'd been certain Brooke was my soulmate, that one special being with whom I connected like no other on the planet. But our time together hadn't been real life. As I'd gotten to know her more, Brooke's faults had bubbled to the surface. In the end, she wasn't so perfect, at all. In the end, she was what we all are: human.

· · ·

The days following my and Naomi's courthouse scene were good ones. We spent time together, being close and talking a lot. We reminisced about the old days, when we'd first met, things we'd done, times we'd had together, how we'd felt about each other, and the dreams we'd had for our future. As we talked, I began to see that somewhere along the way, Naomi and I had gotten lost and gone in different directions. She'd gone one way and busied herself with her life. I'd still had needs, but my wife hadn't been there for me.

"I hated all that time you spent on your damned iPad upstairs!" I told her. "What were you doing—playing Sudoku, Scrabble, or just your mindless internet games, up there?"

She began to laugh. "Maybe sometimes, but mostly, I was just losing myself in another world instead of facing my own. It was just easier. Sometimes I just browsed the sites that turned me on. You know, the whole bondage and tie me up kind of stuff."

"I know what you mean."

I never realized just how blind I was to her needs and wants. If only I had paid attention to her sooner and cleared the air with how I felt and how I wanted to live my life. I had been so tied up into my own wants, needs, and desires that I forgot to communicate with what she wanted or craved. My breath caught and I stopped and stared at this woman who resembled my wife, but whose comment had stupefied me like none other once again.

"Wait. You were looking at the stuff that turns me on as well?" I still couldn't absorb what I'd just heard.

"Yeah, I'm curious. I'm human." She laughed. "Some of that stuff looks pretty interesting, fun even!"

"Holy crap!"

"What? You were downstairs, doing the same thing!" she questioned.

"Well, why in the hell weren't we doing it together? I asked.

"I don't know. Why weren't we?" She laughed.

A lightbulb went on over my head. My world had just opened with infinite possibilities. I could breathe again. My life did not have to be forever vanilla and predictable. There *was* a God and He had smiled upon me! Yet I knew I should proceed with caution. I'd known my wife for many years. I did not want to scare her and send her back into hiding or have her lose interest in me again.

"Um, honey," I casually said, "how would you like trying out some of that stuff you have been casually watching?"

"Sure!"

Hot DAMN! I thought. *And I was about to divorce this woman. What had I been thinking?*

Naomi and I played around and explored this newfound side of her, and of our relationship. It was just what we'd needed. It was new, exciting, and exhilarating, like a breath of fresh air. Our marriage and our relationship felt like it had been infused with new life. Little by little, Naomi agreed to push the limits and try new things in the bedroom. She even seemed to enjoy it as much as I did. She was all in. Not only did she enjoy the new experiences with me; she actively researched new toys and implements to try.

"Hey, so, there's this club," I brought up one night as we lay in bed after an hour of incredible toe-curling sex. "It's kind of a dungeon place, but it's really cool and we can just go and observe if that's all you want to do, but—"

"You went there with *her*, didn't you?"

"That wasn't the only reason I went there."

"But you took *her* there, didn't you?"

"I promised I wouldn't lie to you so, yeah, we did go there. Matter of fact, we found it together. But I think you'd like it. We don't have to go, though, if—"

"No, I'll go. I was just curious. I'll go and check it out," Naomi said.

She was brave and defiant. But a part of me wondered if she wanted to go to the club just so she could find Brooke and rip her limb from limb.

"Uh, hon…the club has a certain decorum for the members, and—"

"I won't hurt her, Alex," she said, laughing. "Not *in* the club."

She got up from the bed and put on her robe to go into the kitchen. I wondered if it was a good idea to risk having Naomi and Brooke in the same room, or even the same building. But let's be honest—a guy who's been ballsy enough to have phone sex with women, with his wife upstairs, and to have cheated on his wife, a few times…well, yeah, that guy would most likely go from the frying pan into the fire.

When Naomi came back to the bedroom, she handed me a drink. "So, what about Friday night?" I asked. "Let's check out the club on Friday night, after dinner."

If she was nervous, she hid it well. Or maybe I had played right into her hand. Maybe she'd wanted to get closer to Brooke. The notion did cross my mind. Women are known for being plotting, conniving, get even types.

"So, what do I wear to this club of yours?" she asked.

"Whatever you want. As much or as little as makes you comfortable. We can just watch or—oh, wait, I just remembered something. We need to get you vetted, first."

"There's a vetting process to go and get your ass beat in public?" She laughed. "I have to pass muster in order to submit to paddling, whipping, flogging, and total surrender in front of a group of strangers?"

"Pretty much. So, you have been watching the online sites!"

"Whatever."

• • •

I took Naomi to a meet-and-greet gathering the club happened to be holding on that Thursday night. It was at a casual restaurant, located elsewhere than the club. The club owner had strict policies, the first being that all new members had to be vetted by the founding members and him before being allowed inside the club. It was his way of attempting to keep out the weirdos and whackos. It helped, but a few still slipped through the cracks now and then. The club was good about removing those types of people, though.

Naomi didn't seem especially nervous about the dinner meeting. It was a non-threatening public venue, and everyone met around a long table. The group might have easily been a church group meeting to discuss some community activism project. We didn't discuss "the club" outside of the club. We were only there to let people meet Naomi and any other new people who wanted to become club members and get vetted among the existing members.

Steve, the club owner, welcomed Naomi and introduced her to the other members around the table. He then introduced another woman who wanted to join. "This is Michele, everyone," Steve said. Since Naomi and Michele were new, they sat together, and I sat beside Naomi, of course. As Steve and I talked, I couldn't help noticing that Michele continued to stare at me, even while Naomi talked to her. I wondered if Naomi noticed. If so, I'd be hearing about it, for sure.

When Michele excused herself and got up to go to the ladies' room, I got a better look at her. She was attractive. Middle-aged, trim, and with a great ass, she definitely caught my eye. But I was there with my wife. It was okay to look, I told myself, but Naomi and I were there together for the club experience, and I had vowed I would try to make things work with us. Ten minutes later, Michele returned. The whole time she walked toward our table, she stared directly at me, as if no one else were in the room. It was a bit uncomfortable, and yet, flattering. I smiled and she smiled back as she took her seat beside Naomi again.

After dinner, Steve invited Naomi to visit the club the next evening or any time she felt comfortable. "Let's go over there tomorrow night," she said to Steve and me. "I want to check it out!" I'd been hoping she'd say that, and I was hoping to use my suitcase of implements and the tools of my new trade in the backseat of my truck. The next day couldn't go fast enough. As we drove toward the club, it was dark outside. "What're you doing?" I asked as Naomi took off her blouse, and then removed her bra, while I drove. "Changing for the club," she said. She pulled out a sheer red lacy tank top thing and slipped it over head as I watched. I wondered who the woman beside me was and what she'd done with my wife. I looked in my rearview mirror and then shifted in my seat. *Was I being punked? Did I dare trust Naomi was so chill about the whole BDSM club thing?*

"What?" She laughed. "You said I could wear as much or as little as I wanted. What do you wear in this place?"

"Um, I—I usually wear a black leather vest."

"Oh, good. Hot. Yeah, I'll like that. No shirt, I hope."

She seemed to be thinking a lot about what to expect, envisioning even what the evening might be. I continued to drive along as my mind also vacillated between this evening's potential intrigue, caution, and titillation. Who was this sexy maven in the seat beside me, and where had she been for so long while I had been thirsting for some excitement?

When we arrived at the club, Naomi didn't seem nervous or uncomfortable at all. She'd put a jacket on over her lace tank top, until we'd gotten inside the doors. But when she removed her jacket, she was still more clothed than most. We signed in. Then I showed her around the club and told her about the various stations and equipment. Since it was a Friday night, the place was fairly busy, mostly with regulars.

As we stood and watched a flogging demonstration, I felt eyes burning a hole in the back of my head and the hairs on the back of my neck stood up, almost like an animal senses danger. Cautiously, I slowly turned around in the dimly lit dungeon, and there she was with her eyes aglow. It was like a scene out of a movie. Her eyes looked red, due to the nearby flickering of candelabras and wall sconces, as they bore a hole through me. Naomi then turned to see what had caught my attention. Just as she did, Brooke spun on her heels and huffed off.

"That's her?" Naomi asked. "Brooke, I presume?"

"Uh, yep. Do you want to go?"

"Go? Why? No way." She laughed as she began to remove her top. "I'm next on the spanking bench."

I realized then it was about to be one of the most bizarre nights of my life. My ex-mistress was forty yards away, and playing the victim, as if I'd torn out her soul, and my wife was stripping down and preparing to allow me to publicly chain and spank her. I wasn't sure whether to be elated or scared to death. Another drink was in order, but Naomi wouldn't wait. She'd already commandeered the nearby spanking bench and was waiting for me. I wasn't going to waste the moment.

As I cuffed and then chained my wife to the spanking table, my heart raced with anticipation. We'd opened a new chapter. But across the dungeon, Brooke watched in cold solace as she nursed her drink and soaked in the comfort of one of the club's founders. God only knew what stories Brooke had told him. But I put her out of mind as I got to work on my wife. She loved her first flogging and spanking session. I could tell by the way her eyes rolled back in her head as she lost herself somewhere between delicious pleasure and pain, entirely unaware of anything but that one stinging spot on the back of her thighs or back. I was careful not to hurt her. In fact, I'd gotten pretty skilled by that time, thanks to some lessons I'd had.

Later in the evening, after Naomi had recovered and was relaxed and sitting on a large sofa, I went and got us more drinks. From across the room, I saw Brooke approaching my wife. Brooke wore that same God-awful white, frumpy negligee I'd hated, the one that made her look just like the Michelin Man. If she'd chosen it for its white, demure color, it had been a huge mistake—and I do mean *huge*. Let's just say the color white doesn't usually do a lot for most middle-aged women, and that garment had lace that appeared to have rolls, just like the Michelin Man. I saw Naomi's face as Brooke approached her. My wife was sizing-up (no pun intended) my former mistress. Naomi looked past Brooke and over at me. Her eyes said what I couldn't hear in her voice: "You nearly ruined your life for *this*?" As Naomi looked at me, I shrugged my shoulders in defeated agreement and rolled my eyes as I leaned on the bar to speak to another club goer.

Minutes later, I went back to Naomi with our water in-hand. Brooke was gone. "What'd she want?" I asked Naomi.

"Oh, she said she'd appreciate it if we wouldn't come down to *her* club," Naomi said.

"What the—" I said as I looked around for Brooke.

"Don't worry," Naomi replied. "I made it clear this is the *first place* we'll be coming, and every chance we get!"

That was my wife. You didn't challenge or screw with her. Brooke should've known that from what I'd told her about Naomi. Nobody told Naomi what to do, especially not when it came to her family.

CHAPTER 16

UNICORNS ARE REAL

Our marriage went along fine, for a while, and Naomi and I did have some great sex. I enjoyed the new, exciting, experimental side of her that she'd revealed to me. I'll admit, though, I wasn't 100 percent sure if Naomi liked the BDSM life or just said she did because she wanted our marriage to work and to keep our family together. Family has always been so important to Naomi, especially since hers was destroyed by divorce. I knew she'd do anything not to cause that kind of pain to our son and daughter. Naomi had always been a great mom, no doubt about it. That was one thing I knew for sure.

After that first night at the club, Naomi and I went back a few times. We saw Michele, the other new woman, there too. Naomi and I both liked Michele. She was pleasant, easy to talk to, funny, and laid back. One night, Michele watched as I flogged Naomi. I saw in Michele's eyes that she was interested, but I knew not to ask Naomi if I could offer to flog Michele. There were some lines I knew not to cross.

Later that night, a female club member said to Naomi, "I don't like your husband."

"What?" Naomi asked, shocked at the woman's sudden rudeness. "Do you even know Alex?"

"Oh, I know all I need to know about that man! Brooke has told all of us about him and what he's about! You people shouldn't even be in here!"

Naomi had told me all about Brooke's comments. But before long, Steve, the club's owner told me that Brooke had circulated some nasty rumors. "Why don't you just lie low?" Steve asked. "Just let the whole thing blow over. Maybe take like six weeks off from the club."

"Are you banning me from the club, Steve?"

"I'm asking you, politely, to give her some space."

Naomi and I referred to that time as being placed on "Exile Island." It wasn't fair, but it turned out to be the best thing that could have happened. Naomi and I invited Michele over to our house, just for dinner and drinks. We had a great time together. We hung out at our place on the lake, grilled out sometimes, played board games or cards, and had drinks. It was nothing sexual, just a good time. The three of us always had a great time together.

Michele had adult kids, even grandkids, we learned. She owned a small business. She was smart too, like Naomi. It was always an easy, comfortable time when we were with one another. I especially loved to come from the office and find Naomi and Michele in the kitchen, sometimes even baking cookies—well, weed cookies. But, still…it was a homey, domesticated, pleasant sight.

"Smells like a dispensary in here!" our nineteen-year-old daughter joked one day when she came in.

"Oh, Mom and Michele are baking again," I said from behind my computer screen.

"Yeah, I've always been just like all the other kids—*not*."

We'd always been fairly open with our kids. Well, once they became young adults, anyway. Naomi and I felt they were glad we'd stayed together, *whatever* that union looked like, since it meant their family was still intact. And I had to admit there must be some benefit to kids seeing real life and knowing their parents are real people who deal with bona fide issues. Our kids even liked Michele and she quickly became a regular in our home.

One night, when it was just Michele, Naomi, and me, I'd gone out to the garage to do something after dinner. The girls had stayed inside and talked over glasses of wine. I could tell Michele had something on her mind; it seemed like she needed some girl-time to talk with Naomi, so I left them to it. An hour later, I came back inside and found the girls sitting on the sofa, with more than half the wine gone, but Michele still looked troubled and stressed.

"What is it?" I asked as soon as I saw both of their faces.

"She needs some relief," Naomi said.

"Relief?"

"Yeah, you know," said Naomi.

"Oh, you mean…me. I should—you're okay if I—," I stammered as I pointed at Naomi, still unsure whether my wife's casual demeanor was some sort of plotted female trickery, devised to catch me off-guard. Caution bells sounded in my head, yellow and red flashing lights went off in my mind, and my brain's computer worked to quickly process the only information it had: the faces of the two women before me. It was one of those conflicted moments where, on one shoulder, an angelic cherub sat, saying, "Alex, you're a married man, a loyal husband who's working on his marriage. You must stay focused and erase those other thoughts from your mind." Yet on the other shoulder sat a little devil—with a raging erection— who said, "Man, are you crazy? This is what every man hopes for and dreams of! Get to it! Your wife is telling you to take this woman to the bedroom, strip her down, and—"

"…and I'm sure it'll help," I heard Naomi say.

Her voice roused me from the battle in my head, or with my conscience—whatever it might've been. Both women stared at me expectantly from the sofa, as if waiting for an answer.

"What? Did you say something?" I asked Naomi.

"I've been explaining to you," she said in an irritated voice that let me know she knew I hadn't been listening, "that Michele is under a lot of pressure lately, just like I was, and I told her I think a good flogging will give her the release she needs."

"Okay. Yes. Okay. I can do that."

I wasn't going to waste the opportunity. I just hoped Naomi was sincere and she'd be okay with having Michele in our bedroom, nearly naked, while I flogged her. Before any of us could change our minds, I headed into the bedroom to set things up.

· · ·

That evening would be the turning point, the time when we'd look back and realize we'd opened a door we could never close, a Pandora's Box, of sorts. But *I* would never want to close that door. *What man would?*

The progression of our relationship was gradual. The dynamics moved slowly, and we were all respectful of one another's positions and feelings. Naomi really enjoyed having Michele as a friend, and Michele liked having Naomi as a friend as well. Michele also enjoyed having me, but I would always be *Naomi's* husband.

After that first night, Michele let me know how much she had enjoyed the flogging. "When you whip me," she tried to explain one night, "it's like I get to release all the crap, all the stress and baggage I've been carrying around. Nothing else matters but that exact space and time. It's such a relief to me. I can't fully explain it, but I crave it."

The three of us spent time talking about it and talking about our friendship and the dynamics of our relationship. There was no doubt I loved Naomi. She'd always be my first love. But I'd begun to feel a pull toward Michele, just in a different way. Was it just sexual? Did she fill some other need in me? Was I finally coming to terms with the person I was always meant to be? Even I wasn't sure. All I knew was I liked where I was in my life.

After I had whipped and flogged Michele a few times, on different occasions, I wondered if Naomi would let things go further. I mean, who'd have ever thought my wife would have ever set foot inside a BDSM club? And I once would have bet my life that Naomi would never be okay with my having another bare-breasted woman, wearing only a thong, in our bedroom. But then came the night when even the thong came off, and I'd placed Michele on the Sybian saddle and turned up the excitement. Ah, the Sybian saddle, a delightful tool in my sexual arsenal of toys. I love how my play partner straddles the leather-bound hump and lowers her body onto the shaft of the upright and firm dildo. Once seated, it only takes a turn of a knob to start the dildo circulating deep within her in a clockwise motion. I can hear the twirl of the motor, and of course, her matching moans to the machine. Now for the fun. With one turn of the other knob, the pad her clit rests on begins to vibrate, and vibrate it does. Moaning in ecstasy and matching the intensity of the vibrating pad, Michele's moans of pleasure were deep and guttural. Just by adjusting the speed and intensity of the vibrations, I could tell when she orgasmed, one after another. I could hear the wetness of her orgasms soak the saddle as I quickly ramped up the speed and then plummeted it down to just a low roar. She must have come about six or seven times. The sweat rolling off her forehead and down her neck was proof enough she was beyond satisfied and exhausted. As Naomi watched the whole thing, the excitement in me became overwhelming. Naomi saw it. Our eyes met as I gently helped Michele slide off the Sybian and onto the carpet. While she was on her knees and bent over, I grabbed onto Michele's sweet ass cheeks to help her steady herself. Looking at her bare ass and open thighs sent a sexual rush through me, an uncontrollable urge just to take her. I looked at Naomi, and without words, I opened my palms and raised my eyebrows, as if to say, "C'mon; it's right there." Naomi nodded and gave me the go-ahead, and I tore off my pants and straddled Michele from behind. Naomi watched as I fiercely pumped into Michele with sexual fury. I looked up and saw that Naomi had grabbed a cordless vibrator and was taking care of herself as I was pounding into Michele, grabbing her pony tail firmly in my left hand as I firmly smacked her ass cheeks with my right. Half an hour later, all three of us were climaxing. My head shot backward; my mind and pent-up animalistic growl exploded in a rush of sexual release. Out of respect for Naomi, I pulled out before I came. Satiated, exhausted, and physically spent, all of us collapsed where we were from exhaustion.

Michele told me later that, when she'd come to the club's vetting dinner, she'd only had eyes for me that night. I was in her crosshairs. But she had also really enjoyed getting to know Naomi, and she was always respectful of Naomi and her feelings. As our trio relationship progressed, we all took it slow. But it was such a natural progression that it seemed relaxed and comfortable for everyone. Even my kids liked Michele, and when they came home to visit, they were always comfortable that she was there, even on weekends.

Having Michele around may have helped Naomi to heal over Brooke, in a weird way. The two women bonded and had their own relationship, just as friends, never anything more. In fact, even as time moved on, there never was anything sexual between Michele and Naomi. As I became more well-versed in our arrangement, I found that Michele was what is called a "unicorn" in our threesome relationship. In polyamory, a unicorn is the third person who's in the trio, with the full consent of all people involved.

Michele became a part of our unit. But we didn't tell anyone of our arrangement, of course. One day, Michele reported to us a conversation she's had with her nineteen-year-old son. "Mom," he had confronted her, "I have come to the conclusion that you have been over at Alex and Naomi's a lot, and spending the weekends there too." His tone was disapproving. "Don't lie to me, Mom. Are you screwing Alex? Because he's married, and if you are, you're going straight to hell!"

That was a difficult one. "Well, son," Michele had replied, "I'm not going to lie to you. So, yes, I am. But it's not what you think, not what it looks like. Naomi's aware of what's going on. Let's just say we are all adults and we are happy. I am the happiest I have been in a very, very long time." With that said, he followed up with an "Okay" and continued about his business.

Another time, when Michele and Naomi had been dressed and ready to head out to the club, my adult daughter had stopped by. "Mom, hold on; open your shirt," she'd said. "What have you got on under there? Are you headed to a swingers' club? Oh, my God!"

Naomi didn't lie to her daughter, either. "No, I'm not heading to a swingers' club; calm down." Well, it wasn't a swingers' club. It was a BDSM club, but she didn't need to know that either.

We all knew that not everyone would understand our lifestyle, nor was it anyone else's business what we did behind closed doors. The three of us were happy and that was what mattered. Frankly, it was the first time I'd been happy in as long as I could remember. I hadn't realized what my life was missing until I found it. Naomi, Michele, and I spent weekends together, went out together, and even went on vacations together.

Life was good, very good. In time, the three of us returned to the BDSM club and played there a bit. One night, while inside the club, I felt that uncomfortable burning again in the back of my head. Before my head could spontaneously combust, I quickly turned around. Sure enough, it was Brooke. Her eyes were laser-focused and searing into me, but beside her were two more of her female minions who sucked their teeth and squinted their eyes as they looked me up and down.

"Stay here. I've got this," Naomi said as she left the wax demonstration and walked toward the coven of witches who held their arms firmly crossed. Brooke walked away when she saw Naomi headed her way, but the other two stayed. One said to Naomi, "We don't care for your husband, you know."

"No one gives a damn. You know?" Naomi replied. "Excuse me."

And with that, she went to find Brooke, not willing to let her get away. She easily found my prior mistress, standing off to the side, and wearing some bizarre frumpy negligee that looked like something out of her Aunt Beatrice's closet. "Brooke, do you have a minute?" Naomi asked. Brooke didn't reply, but she fell in step and followed Naomi like a prisoner being led to the gallows. They went into an adjoining room, and I watched from afar as Brooke's two sister witches scurried over to join her, afraid they might miss something.

I kept an eye on the entrance to the nearby room, but Naomi didn't come out. Finally, she emerged, and as she scanned the room for me, I waved to get her attention. I walked toward her and met her in the middle of the room, near a submissive auction scene.

"Well, should I get the car quickly? Are you going into witness protection right away?" I asked, almost afraid to know what had just transpired.

"That bitch is diabolical," said Naomi, laughing. "What the hell were you thinking?"

She told me that the two women had swooped in and stood on either side of Brooke like bookends. One had started in on Naomi, saying, "We can't stand your husband! We all know how he treated Brooke!"

Naomi snapped back at the minions and told them they'd only heard the story from one, and that they didn't know her husband and shouldn't be making assumptions. She turned on Brooke and told her, "I've had about enough of this victim charade you've been playing! The only victim in all this is *me*!"

I felt guilty when Naomi told me that. She was right. She had been the only victim, and I'd put her in that position. Brooke had merely been in the right place, at the right time. I had once found her attractive and special, but not now. She had simply filled a need, a hole, a cavity in my soul. To be honest, I had done the same for Brooke. She'd always wanted to be someone she was not. She'd wanted to live above her means. She'd wanted to dine in fancy restaurants, drink fine wines, take nice trips, wear designer labels, and be looked upon by others as a wealthy, successful woman. When she'd been with me, I had provided her with those things. But they'd been just props, and she'd merely been an actor, temporarily playing a role she simply was not qualified to fill. Just like Naomi and I had

gone to the sex club to play out our scenes and have our fun, Brooke
had briefly gotten to play out scenes with me and try on a life she
would not get to keep for herself, at least not with me.

Naomi, Michele, and I continued to enjoy our own scenes in
the club. But we usually did our scenes with the spanking bench or
the cross, and then we returned home, smoked a little weed, and
had amazing sex. After some time, we thought, "Hey, we've pretty
much got our dungeon at home. Why not just stay home and have
our fun?"

As I said, much earlier, I'd always been that guy with all the
newest toys and gadgets, the one with all the lake toys, the newest
Jet Skis, the latest electronics, gizmos, and appliances. Well, needless to say, I was also that guy with all the coolest, newest sex toys.
You name it, I probably had it, and I'd wanted my girls to have the
best. I was, after all, a considerate Dom who also cared about his
subs' experiences. As I came into my own and began to embrace my
newfound identity as a dominant man, I found I was very comfortable with my sexuality. Therefore, I had no problem with the ladies
enjoying their sexual fun, too.

I'd never been one of those Doms who'd been into blood play,
boot stomping a submissive as she lay on the ground, or the painful
behaviors that, in my opinion, are nothing more than downright
abuse. Oddly, the further I got away from Brooke, the more clearly
I saw my one-time mistress. What had I been thinking? What had I
ever seen in her? One night, while surfing a fetish site on the computer, I came across the profile of the person she'd started dating
after we broke up. I am entirely liberal about sexuality, but even
I was stupefied by this person's sexual predilections. Brooke was
with an individual who currently identified as a male, but was born
a female. That part, I understood. What blew my mind was that

this person was a crazed, boot-stomping bitch, who put on heavy steel-toed boots, threw Brooke to the floor, and publicly kicked her. Nothing about that sounded fun or sexually arousing to me. But to each his own. In a way, I even felt sorry for Brooke that she'd begun a relationship with such a person. In time, we learned Brooke married him. I wondered if she wore her white Michelin Man lacey number on her wedding night.

CHAPTER 17

UNCHAINED

With our son out of the house and our daughter moved out and off to college, it became easier to be freer with our sex life. We even got to the point where we told the kids, "Hey, don't come home next weekend. We've got plans," and they didn't dare take a chance and pop in, lest they might have to gouge out their eyes after accidentally witnessing something they couldn't un-see.

"Your birthday's coming up soon," Michele said to me one night over dinner. "How old will you be?"

"After fifty, do we still count?" I asked, laughing.

"Well, don't make any plans for that weekend. We've got some plans of our own for you."

I had hoped the girls had been plotting. My last birthday had been one to remember. Hell, I didn't even mind getting a year older if it meant a blowout like they'd given me the year before. I could hardly wait for the calendar pages to turn for the next one. I felt like a kid again.

"Hey, whose turn is it to go first on the Sybian tonight?" Naomi asked as I ate the chocolate cake Michele had brought over for dessert. "Michele and I need to get ours since it'll be all about you on your birthday weekend!"

"You girls like that thing, don't you?"

"If only it would mow my lawn," Michele said, wistfully, "it'd be the perfect man!"

"That thing cost more than my first car!" Naomi laughed. "And it rides better, too!"

"And it's been driven more *miles*!" Michele added.

That was our relationship. We always had a good time, always laughed and joked. But once we closed the door, I always took total control. I loved the dynamics between all of us. There were the times, however, when Naomi offered her two cents about what Michele might need to increase her pleasure during one of our sessions. It was interesting to have the perspective of another female, and Naomi always got off on watching Michele. Even when we'd been in the club, and I had put both women on facing crosses, restrained and able to see one another, Naomi's experience was heightened by being able to see Michele. Plus, Naomi could always get into Michele's head during our sessions by saying, "Oh, no! I'm so sorry! He's got the big paddle out! This one's gonna really hurt, girl!" That was part of the fun—the build-up and the anticipation.

Naomi and Michele had their fun, too, with the build-up and anticipation for my birthday. In the days leading up to it, I could tell they were up to something. It was definitely a time we'd told the kids not to plan to visit for the weekend, but beyond that, I hadn't a clue what to expect.

When Friday arrived, I went to work as usual and then headed home, eager for my weekend play to begin. I felt certain Michele would already be at the house, and I was right. When I walked in, the girls were ready and waiting, each wearing a long floor-length cream-colored kimono, and facing the door expectantly. Neither wore a bra, and their nipples were at attention as they rubbed against the soft silk fabric. "Now, this is the greeting I expect every evening!" I laughed.

"Happy Birthday, sir," the girls said in unison as they both came and flanked me to lead me into the living room.

I was eager to play along and melt into my role. Soft Asian-inspired music played from the speakers overhead and the lights were dimmed everywhere. Candles were lit throughout the house. "Would you like to sit, sir?" Naomi asked as she waved her hand toward the recliner, which was covered with a large silk sheet. As I started to sit, Naomi gently stopped me. She began to unbutton my shirt, and then Michele pulled it off from behind me as Naomi began undoing my belt buckle and then my pants. Michele bent down to remove my shoes, and then they both slipped my pants down, but left my underwear on. My erection had already joined the party, not wanting to miss a moment, but the girls were ignoring it. I'd play along—for a little while.

"Sir, we've selected a special birthday whiskey, just for you," Michele said. As she picked up a nearby bottle, I instantly recognized the antler logo.

"Ladies, nice! Wow! But you girls really shouldn't have gone so overboard like this! This is crazy-good—but crazy-expensive!"

"Only the best for our Dom," Naomi said as she winked at me.

Both of the girls knew I liked George T. Stagg Kentucky Straight Bourbon Whiskey. Yet I felt certain they'd spent around $700 for that bottle of hearty whiskey that was, at minimum, aged fifteen years and straight out of the barrel and unfiltered. When Michele handed me a glass of it, I inhaled and savored the blends of sweet toffee and dark chocolate, with nougat and molasses, and touches of tobacco, berries, mint, and just a bit of coffee.

"The man at the store said this one is *powerful, flavorful*, and *intense*," Michele said. "Naomi and I said that described *you* perfectly. Happy Birthday, Alex."

I laughed at the description as I took a sip and held it in my mouth for a minute. As I allowed the whiskey to slowly run down my throat, my mouth and throat warmed. I considered what Michele had said: powerful, flavorful, and intense. I liked that. I sat back in my chair, shut my eyes, and settled in to enjoy the excellent whiskey. As the music continued to play, Naomi started to gently stroke my hand and arm. On the other side of my chair, Michele did the same to my opposite arm, the one that held the glass. Gently, lightly, they stroked and tenderly kneaded my hands and arms as I relaxed and let the whiskey warm me on the inside. Minutes later, Naomi stood up and went behind my chair. She began to stroke my head and my cheeks, as she stood behind me, and she gently used to send chills through my body. Michele's soft hands stroked my chest and my arms. For a few minutes, they took their time and let me enjoy the unhurried pace as I sipped my whiskey. Then the girls were on either side of me again, each lightly massaging one of my legs. My erection was straining and standing at attention now, eager to be seen and paid some notice. I reached down and pulled Naomi's kimono off her shoulders so that it fell down and exposed her breasts, but was still tied at her waist. Then I did the same to Michele's kimono and watched as both bare-breasted women massaged my legs. I had told two of my male friends about the arrangement Naomi and I had with Michele; as I watched the scene in front of me, I wished I could send a photo of it to the guys. They'd have been so insanely jealous. I had one friend who had sex maybe twice a month. When he'd asked me how often I'd been getting it, and I had replied, "Like sixteen times a week," he'd nearly spit out his food in utter shock. "*A week? What're you, some kind of machine?*" he had asked, laughing. "I do have what we lovingly refer to as 'boner pills,'" I replied, laughing also. "But you've got to understand, I have two women to satisfy now." "Shut up, you damned showoff," my friend had scoffed, "and *you* can get the check."

My eyes had been closed so I hadn't seen Naomi grab the warm bottle of oil. She massaged it into my legs, and Michele did the same. Their soft, smooth hands slid up and down my legs with ease through the warm oil. As they leaned into my legs, their nipples touched my skin ever so lightly and glistened in the candlelight from the oil. I sipped my whiskey and leaned back to watch the girls.

Finally, mercifully, warm, oiled hands reached into the leg holes of my underwear and massaged my scrotum. Wordlessly, Michele pulled my underwear off to free my throbbing cock from its prison. I could have stayed right there forever. I had found Utopia, and it was right in my own living room. I groaned with pleasure as four hands, twenty fingers, rubbed, massaged, slid, and explored. For a guy who'd missed out on so much in college, I sure was making up for it now. When I "blew out my candles," I yelled so loud the dog howled in the next room and then ran and hid under a bed for the rest of the night—and that lab had seen and heard some stuff, let me tell you.

• • •

After a shower, we all dressed and went out to dinner. We had recently bought two discreet, personal vibrators for the girls, and I had synced their controls to my cell phone. Naomi and Michele thought it would be fun if we used them that night. "Locked and loaded, ladies?" I asked when we'd gotten into the car to leave the house. "Mine is in," Naomi said. "Mine's in, too. Bring it on!" Michele laughed. While I drove, I tried the controls on my phone, just to make sure my phone would control the vibrators the ladies had already inserted inside themselves.

"Here it comes, Naomi," I said. "Feel good?"

"Woe! Back off, cowboy! Yeowww!"

We all laughed, as I turned my attention to Michele's device. "It's all you now, Michele."

"Good grief!" she said.

"That speed is called Climbing the Walls," I said, laughing.

"I can see why!"

"Naomi, what've we done? We've created a monster by giving him the control!" Michele joked.

An hour later, we sat in a restaurant, in a wood booth connected to another booth, configured as part of one big unit. While the girls' nether regions were pleasantly vibrating, the waitress came over to take our orders. I looked down at my phone, as if texting or reading something. The waitress asked Michele, "How would you like that steak cooked?"

"Medium raaaaaaaaare," she squealed as the wide-eyed waitress leaned away from her.

"Yes, ma'am," the waitress said, almost afraid of Michele. Then she turned her attention to Naomi. "Would you like to start with an appetizer?"

Naomi glanced at me, as if to tell me to play it cool. But I was having fun. Naomi said, "Yes, I'd like an appetizer, please. I'll try the mmmmmmozzarella sticks."

Michele and I tried so hard not to laugh. We felt like teenagers as we tried to hold in our laughter. Naomi looked like she wanted to kill me. The waitress looked so uncomfortable.

Naomi took a deep breath. Her face was red, and her brow was sweating. She was afraid to speak. But she tried again, quickly saying, "I'll have the catch of the day." She closed her menu and handed it to the waitress, who asked, "Rice pilaf or baked potato?"

Naomi glanced at me first. I was still looking down at my phone. Naomi said, "Make it the potatooooooo!"

People at the table across from us looked over, and another waitress walked by trying to figure out what was happening. Our poor waitress still had to deal with me. "Sir, what may I bring you?"

"Oh, I'll have what *she's* having!" I joked as I winked and handed her my menu. "No sour cream on that potato, please."

For the remainder of the meal, I toyed with the speed of the girls' vibrators, using my synced cell phone. Michele leaned in and whispered to me that she was pretty sure the whole booth was vibrating, including the people's seats behind us, since the girls' seats were connected to other people's seats. But I only enjoyed the situation even more. At one point, as both vibrators were synchronized, I had the control's intensity at almost the highest speed, and both Naomi and Michele were unable to carry on conversations. I was almost afraid someone might think Naomi was in the throes of a seizure as she grabbed the tablecloth, gritted her teeth, slunk down in our booth, and rolled her eyes back in her head. At the same moment, Michele had stopped eating. She'd buried her face in my shoulder, at first, but then she stretched her legs out straight under the table and held onto the edge of the booth's bench seat. She clamped her mouth shut and was making gurgling, guttural sounds as her hips pushed back hard against the seat. It was all I could do not to burst into laughter as I controlled the speed of their orgasms with my cell phone. I loved technology!

By the time the waitress came back to see if we wanted dessert, the girls had barely eaten. Yet they looked like they'd just run a marathon. Both red and sweaty, their hair matted to their heads, their clothes disheveled from clutching them. "I think they'd like you to wrap their dinners to go," I told the waitress. "Guess they weren't as hungry as they'd thought."

When we had to get up to walk out, I had to help the girls up. Other diners probably thought Naomi and Michele had been drinking. They were sauced all right, but not by alcohol; they were just fuck drunk. Their legs were wobbly, and it was difficult for them to walk. "I'm going to kill you, Alexander!" Naomi whispered as she leaned on me. "Aw, c'mon. It's my birthday!" "I'm going to help her kill you, Alexander!" Michele added as she held my other arm to steady herself. "That was not funny."

• • •

The next day of my birthday weekend started out with all three of us in Naomi's and my king-sized bed. But Naomi's not a morning person. She's the slower one to wake, the one who likes her morning time. She prefers to lazily greet the day and meander into the kitchen to start the coffee, with one eye half-shut. But I'm a guy who generally wakes with morning wood and looks for a way to relieve it. That's where Michele came in. On this day, Saturday, I woke at 5:30 a.m.—or, I should say, my erection woke me and told me to "Wake someone to find me some relief, and quick; I'm tired of waiting." Always eager to join him, I turned toward Michele, on my left, and nuzzled her while Naomi slept on my right. Michele was always willing to have sex, at the drop of a hat, any time, day or night. She had a hearty sexual appetite, and I liked that about her. But we didn't want to wake Naomi, so we quietly slipped out of bed and found a spot on the floor where we'd thought Naomi couldn't hear us. Michele grabbed an extra blanket from beside the bed and brought it with us. But try as we might to be quiet and considerate, my silent bedroom soon sounded like a cross between running in wet flip-flops and squeaky windshield washers on their highest setting. About an hour later, Michele and I rejoined Naomi and fell back asleep for a couple of hours until the smell of fresh coffee woke me. When I opened my eyes, I was alone. The girls were obviously already up.

"Morning," Naomi said as she came in with a mug of hot coffee. "So, did you have an orgasm earlier?"

I wasn't sure how to answer that question. I knew I could be in dangerous territory. Those innate alarm bells sounded again and the caution lights flashed, sort of like what happens at a railroad crossing. But Naomi stood there, waiting for my answer, as she held my mug of coffee.

"Well, did you?"

"Uh, yeah," I hesitated.

"Oh, good. Here."

She turned and went into the bathroom. Was I okay? Was this a trap, one of those women's traps? Was she getting a weapon in there? What did that mean? Those three little words: *Oh, good, here.* What the hell did that mean?

"Good? Did you say '*good*,' Naomi?" I called into the bathroom as I heard the sound of her electric toothbrush.

She stepped out to look at me, and pulled the toothbrush out of her mouth as she looked up toward the ceiling just a bit, "Yeah, I'm glad. Good. You needed it."

I took a drink of my coffee, almost afraid to believe my good fortune. Had my wife just acknowledged that it was acceptable for me to now orgasm inside another woman? I jokingly let my mind wander to whether Naomi and Michele could possibly have a thing, their own clandestine lesbian relationship, unbeknownst to me. Maybe they were trying to throw me off-guard, let me get comfortable, and eventually, they'd bump me off and take the lakefront house, the investments, and the life insurance, and live happily ever after. Let's be honest; I could be a giant ass at times, and Naomi and Michele *were* good friends. I had seen that, for sure. Okay, so I'll admit I'd seen a few of those Lifetime Channel movies. Stranger things have happened, though. But I'd wager that if I told a hundred men that my wife had just given me the thumbs-up for fully completed, mind-blowing orgasmic sex with another woman in our marital bedroom, *all* of those men would tell me to watch my back! Now, which storyline sounds more bizarre?

"Birthday Boy!" Michele called. "You up? Because you were up a few hours ago, that's for sure."

She came into the bedroom with a tray of croissants, Danish pastries, and glasses of juice she placed on the bed for all three of us. She crawled onto the bed, came over beside me, kissed me on the cheek, and whispered so Naomi wouldn't hear from the bathroom.

"She heard us, didn't she? Is she okay?"

"She's good, yeah."

"Whew. Okay."

Michele and I had always tried to be considerate of Naomi and her feelings. We knew ours was an unusual arrangement. From my perspective, I didn't want to do anything to screw up the good thing that had been going on. I wasn't an idiot. Michele, from what I could tell anyway, had begun to have feelings for me and wanted to remain a part of our trio. And Naomi, I hoped, was getting what she'd wanted, too: her marriage and her intact family, and also some sexual exploration and fun. Yet we were dealing with people and emotions. So we tried to tread lightly in all things.

"What on today's agenda, ladies?" I asked as I took a juice glass from Michele. "Thanks, hon."

"Wouldn't you like to know?" Naomi said as she came into the bedroom to join us. "But the first thing on the agenda will be to hide the remote-control Lush vibrators from you!"

"Oh, come on now. That older grandmother in the booth behind you looked very happy!"

• • •

After we'd all been up for a bit, I said, "Hey, do we have an hour or so?"

"Yeah, I guess," Michele shrugged, and Naomi nodded in agreement.

"Let's go try out the new Motor Bunny Buck machine, girls."

It took no convincing. Those two loved our toys and gadgets, especially the Sybian saddle. I'd just bought the Motor Bunny Buck, a similar contraption, but the vibrating dildo on the new one also thrusted, in addition to vibrating. I had a whole scene already worked out in my head, and I couldn't wait to act it out. But first, we smoked a bit, just to relax everyone even more.

"You, two," I said, laughing.

"What?" Naomi asked.

"The way you're looking at that Sybian saddle, it's like you're enamored with it."

"It's changed my life!" Naomi laughed.

"No, *I've* changed your life!" I reminded her, as I grabbed her, tore off her shirt, and then bound her wrists with a leather strap. "Let me remind you so you'll never forget!"

Next, I blindfolded her. Then I took her by her upper arm and led her toward the middle of our bedroom. I reached up and attached her wrists to the chain that hung down from the hook I'd had previously installed behind a secret smoke detector cover. Michele silently watched, eager, I knew, for her turn.

"You're next." I winked as I went to her and pulled her shirt off, also revealing her bare breasts. "Let me remind you, too, of how I've changed your life as well!"

I knew Michele was moist just at the thought. She was one kinky bitch, that crazy nymphomaniac that guys dream of finding. I took her nearer to Naomi, blindfolded her, bound her wrists, and connected them to another chain that hung from the ceiling, this one from behind what looked to be a security system motion detector. The women were about seven feet apart and facing each other, both still wearing lounge pants. I went to Naomi and lightly ran my fingers round the sides of her round, ample breasts. Then I licked and nibbled on her pert nipples as they strained and begged for my touch. She leaned her head back and moaned as I put my hands into her pants and onto her ass. Then I slid her pants off as I ran my tongue down her body, stopping to kiss and lightly bite her flesh at different intervals.

I let Michele listen to Naomi's moans of pleasure. I knew the anticipation drove her crazy, and it was usually Naomi who manipulated Michele and screwed with her during the roleplay at the dungeon, so, I let Michele wait—and wonder. Next, I went and got the Sybian, Naomi's favorite toy. I swear she would have chosen it over a Lamborghini, if given the choice; that's how much she loved that thing. I rolled it in on its portable stand and moved it closer to the woman who used to be my demure, vanilla, predictable wife.

I turned it on so she could hear it—but I wouldn't let her mount it, not yet.

"Hey, am I being forgotten?" Michele asked.

"Did I tell you to speak?" I barked, just to let her know we were very much in our roles and the sex play had begun.

"No, sir. My apologies."

Sometimes, I used a gag with my subs. It all depended upon my mood and the scene I felt like playing out. This time, I wanted to hear their pleasure sounds so I left the gags off—for now. If I felt like it, I was sure I could always find *something* like their panties to shove in their mouths.

While Naomi listened to the familiar sounds of her beloved Sybian and ached to feel it vibrating deep inside her loins, I went over to my impatient, second submissive. I grabbed her hair and pulled it backward; then I spoke in her ear with hot breath, "Are you a horny bitch?"

"Yes, yes, Master," she sighed as her breasts heaved.

While I held her hair, twisted in my fist, I gently nibbled on her right nipple. As she relaxed and sighed, I sucked hard and then harder until she winced.

"You don't ever rush the Master!" I said as I let go of her hair. "Do not speak!"

I said nothing else to her as I walked out of the room to get what I needed. A few minutes later, I was back. It gave me great satisfaction to see both women waiting there for me, for whatever I wanted to do with them, at my beck and call, to be used at my whim. It was a heady, omnipotent feeling, one that's difficult to convey in words. Since I'd found out I was a dominant, my whole world had changed. I walked through life differently and was on a constant power high. The sight of Naomi and Michele, bare-breasted, blindfolded, and chained to the ceiling, helpless and at my disposal, filled me with something herculean that defied all explanation. Yet at the same time, I'd never hurt either of those two women. In fact, we'd agreed a long time earlier on a safe word, a certain word that, when said by anyone, would end all play, immediately. The girls knew I'd respect our agreement. We had that trust.

When I returned to the bedroom again, I had the new Motor Bunny Buck, along with a few other props. Silently, I went about my work. I plugged in the new vibrating, thrusting dildo on a saddle, and placed it beside Michele. Then, I put some water-based lubricant on each of the dildos for the girls. (I'm *not* a barbarian!) Next, I took out the nipple clamps and connected chains to them. I went back to Naomi, pinched her right nipple so it would become erect, and then clipped a nipple clamp onto it. She winced a bit, surprised by the pinch. She knew the next one was coming—and she was right. With about six feet of lightweight chain between the women, I repeated the process, clipping nipple clamps to Michele, crossing the chains in an X between the women.

"Okay, girls, you're connected now by chains. Don't pull too hard and pull the clamps off each other, okay?"

I went first to Naomi and pulled the Sybian closer to her. When I put my hand between her legs, I laughed. "Should've known!" I said. "No coconut oil needed for you!" She couldn't wait to mount up. Naomi slid onto the vibrating rotating dildo and sat firmly on the saddle as she took it all inside, all at once. Then, I went to

Michele and guided her onto her own pulsating, thrusting lifelike penis. Michele's was our newest toy that we were trying out for the first time. It was just like the Sybian, only it had the thrusting feature. So I figured the girls would compare notes later on how their mounts had performed.

"Okay, bitches, here's the rule!" I yelled over the sounds of the vibrating machine. "You're both connected by a chain. No matter what, do not pull the other's clamp off of her or there will be severe penalties!"

I sat down and watched as the women had no control, but I did. They couldn't touch their bodies, but I could. They couldn't see one another, but I could. They grinded and gyrated and bucked their hips, but only I could turn up the speed and take them to that glorious release. After a few minutes, I went over and turned up the speed, first for Michele, and then for Naomi. They both rode their saddles like champs, deeper, faster, harder. Naomi's face and neck were bright red, and she moaned and grimaced. Michele bucked and arched her back as she grinded deeper and deeper, finding just that special hidden spot within the hidden recesses. Michele and Naomi both moaned and fed off each other, as I watched the chain between them become taut and straight. And then it went loose again. And then tight. And then slack.

"Oh, oh, ohhhhhhh!" Michele arched her back and pulled away as her head leaned back. Suddenly, the clamp on Naomi's left nipple pulled away and the chain fell to the floor.

"Oh, my—oh—oh my—aaaahhhhh…." Naomi's knees tightened on the saddle and she leaned back as her nipples stood fully erect.

I jumped up and tore off my pants, hard and ready. I went to Michele, limp and spent, and pulled her off the saddle. "I told you there would be punishment if you pulled it off! Didn't I tell you that?" While she was still chained to the ceiling, I stood behind her and slightly bent her forward. As much as the slack at her wrists would allow, I rammed her from behind, hard and deep, all at once. I held her hips and punished her full force as her spent body helplessly gave itself over to me, gushing all the while.

. . .

Later that night, after we'd returned from dinner, I was in the living room when Michele called for me from the bedroom. I couldn't possibly imagine the girls were up for more sex since we'd had a lot of it already during the weekend. But when I got to the bedroom, it was transformed and so were Naomi and Michele. They wore matching sheer black robes, and Michele had on a hot pink thong and Naomi wore a purple thong. Between their breasts, they each had a gemstone, connected to their nipples by chains and clips, some sort of sexy body jewelry. A warming massage table and some heating stones were waiting for me. Incense burned and candles were lit all around the room.

"We thought it might be a nice way to end the evening," Naomi said, smiling.

I was already removing my clothes.

"First, lie on your stomach," Michele said as she held up a sheet so I could lie down on the waiting massage table.

For at least an hour, the girls massaged just my backside, from head to toe. It felt like I'd died and gone to Heaven. They placed hot stones on my back, all the way down onto my ass, to relax me, and then they used the stones to massage my skin, in addition to using their hands with scented oil. After a good hour, they told me to turn over because there was another glass of that excellent whiskey for me. So, I had a couple of sips before I lay down on my back, face up this time.

After another hour of relaxing massage, Naomi began massaging my scrotum, just lightly. As she did that, Michele put her mouth on my cock, ever so lightly though, just so her hot breath heated it and made me ache for more. I moaned as I spread my legs and Michele began to suck harder. Naomi then bent down and ran her tongue over my scrotum; she took my balls into her mouth and lightly sucked. I thought I'd go out of my mind. But then the girls switched and my cock was in the back of Naomi's throat; Michele's tongue was between my legs, sending me over the edge, as her fingertips expertly kneaded my scrotum. I held both of their heads against my groin and leaned back as my eyes rolled back in my head. The girls kept switching as I held their heads in my hands, their hair wrapped round my hands. At times, I didn't even know whose mouth my cock was in; I just knew I was in ecstasy as their mouths worked the shaft and teased the tip with skills I didn't even know existed. I was lost in the waves of pleasure that washed over me as the girls alternated back and forth and up and down until I couldn't hold back any longer.

"Happy Birthday, sir," Michele said.

"Happy Birthday, Master," Naomi said.

• • •

We went to bed later that night, all three of us, together in my king-sized bed in the master bedroom of the home Naomi and I had shared for years, the same one I'd grown up in. But the man who lay between the two women in that bed was so different from the one who used to live in that house. Gone was the quiet, uncertain guy who didn't feel like he'd fit in, and who'd always felt he was on the outside, looking in. In his place, was a dominant, take-charge man who grabbed the world by the balls. I liked the new guy so much better.

Naomi and Michele had already fallen asleep. They'd had such a busy weekend. I looked to my right and saw Naomi sleeping, and to my left, and saw Michele asleep. Each was nestled in the crook of one of my arms, facing me with a hand on my chest. What more could I ask for in my life?

"What a blessed life," I whispered as I shut my eyes, grateful, happy, and content with my dominant world, but most of all, **UNCHAINED**.

Made in the USA
Monee, IL
13 October 2020